Home

Challenging maths   1

Challenging maths   1

C. E. L. Farmer and M. C. Swash
Ounsdale Comprehensive School, Wombourn, Staffordshire

J. W. Baxter
Castle Vale Comprehensive School, Birmingham

McGraw-Hill Publishing Company Limited
LONDON · New York · Toronto · Sydney · Mexico ·
Johannesburg · Panama · Singapore

Published by
McGraw-Hill Publishing Company Limited
McGraw-Hill House, Maidenhead, Berkshire, England

07 094370 2

Printed and bound in Great Britain

Preface

This book is the first in a series designed for use in Secondary Schools.
The series is intended to provide suitable preparation for pupils wishing to
take mathematics at the Certificate of Secondary Education level. The
early books in the series provide a good basic mathematics course which
can later be developed in the way suggested by the Newsom Report.

In preparing this series, we have been influenced by international move-
ments in the realm of mathematics, and, in particular, by the work of
experimental groups in this country. The series represents our interpreta-
tion of the new trends in mathematics teaching as they apply to pupils in
Secondary Schools. We have sought to present the material in a way which
will stimulate the pupil to an understanding of mathematical principles
and to a desire to undertake mathematical activity.

Anticipating the changes in U.K. currency and units of measure, decimal
currency and metric units have been used throughout the series.

The following abbreviations have been used when appropriate:
metre, m; kilometre, km; millimetre, mm; centimetre, cm; gramme, g;
kilogramme, kg; hour, h; minute, min; and second, s.

This first book provides a comprehensive one-year course. We suggest that
the chapters are taken in order and that all the practical activities are
undertaken. We have assumed throughout this text that pupils will be
provided with five millimetre graph paper.

We wish to express our appreciation to Mr Brian Drury of Mount Pleasant
Comprehensive School, Birmingham, who has read through the manu-
script and made a number of valuable suggestions; also to our publisher
for the interest and co-operation received at all stages in the writing and
production processes.

C. E. L. Farmer
M. C. Swash
J. W. Baxter

Acknowledgements

The authors and publisher wish to thank the following for permission to use the material specified:

The drawing of a chicken (quadriside) on page 47 reproduced from *Mathematics Teaching*, Number 27, Summer 1964, published by the Association of Teachers of Mathematics. The origami model on pages 54 and 55 reproduced from *The Art of Origami* by Samuel Randlett, published by Faber and Faber.

The diagram of the desk calculating machine on page 22, Olympic Business Machines Co. Ltd.; the map on page 130, the Automobile Association and Ordnance Survey.

Contents

1. Collecting, sorting, and arranging   *p 1*

2. Number patterns   *p 20*

3. About shape   *p 38*

4. About size   *p 56*

5. Composition tables   *p 72*

6. Strange arithmetic   *p 89*

7. Balancing   *p 106*

8. From ordered pairs to graphs   *p 130*

9. Playing with squares   *p 144*

10. Smaller than one, and other fractions   *p 160*

11. Turning in circles   *p 172*

12. Let's find out about statistics   *p 198*

13. Checking up   *p 208*

Test papers   *p 233*

1. Collecting, sorting, and arranging

Materials required

Three sets (one blue, one white, one black) each consisting of:

three triangles (one isosceles, one equilateral, one scalene)

three quadrilaterals (one square, one rectangle, one parallelogram)

two circles (different diameters).

1.1

Sort your collection of coloured shapes into different sets, each set having something in common. For example, all the same colour or all the same shape.

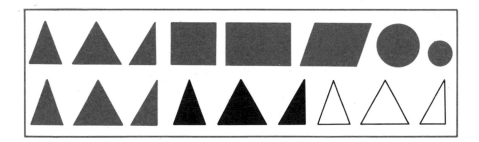

Make a note of all the sets you can make. The largest number of simple sets that you can make from your shapes is twenty-three. How many did you make?

1.2

Here are some more collections. Look at them carefully and say which have some common feature and which have not. Can you give names to any of the sets?

1*

1.3

Discuss with your friends and your teacher other things which are collected in sets, for example, postage stamps, birds' eggs, train numbers, etc. Bring examples of sets to school. Have the sets any common feature? What names do you give the sets? Can they be rearranged to make different sets in the same way that your coloured shapes could?

1.4

Make up wall charts showing some of the different sets you have found. Also show any sets you made by rearranging other sets.

1.5

Which of the following have a common feature. What name would you give to each set?
(1) birch, yew, oak, ash, – – –
(2) George, Paul, Tom, John, – – –
(3) turnip, carrot, swede, potato, – – –
(4) stone, moon, water, cow
(5) pink, orange, mauve, green, – – –
(6) 1, 3, 5, 7, 9, 11, – – –.
The dashes after the last member of the set indicate that there are other members of the set which have not been written down.

Give the names of three members of each of the following sets:
(1) birds   (2) coins
(3) postage stamps   (4) animals with three legs
In listing the elements of a set, each element is written once only.
For example, in (1) you would not write 'swallow, swallow,
swallow', but three different types of bird.

1.7
When we are writing about sets, we usually put curly brackets { }
round the set, for example, {birds}. The brackets stand for 'the set
of '. Thus {birds} is read as 'the set of birds'.

1.8
Name the members of the following sets:
(1) {days of the week}   (2) {whole numbers between 0 and 12}

1.9
If you take the collection of shapes with which you started and pick
out {black cards} you will see that it contains three different sorts
of shape:

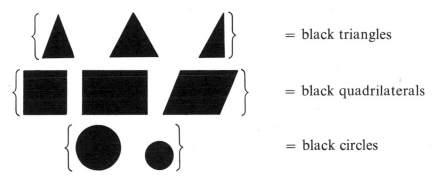

= black triangles

= black quadrilaterals

= black circles

So, inside {black cards} there are three other sets.

1.10
Now lay out {blue cards} and {white cards}: see if the same is true.

1.11
We have a special name for sets which are part of a larger set, they
are called subsets. For example, {black triangles} is a subset of
{black cards}.

To save writing 'is a subset of ' we use the symbol ⊂.
Thus, instead of writing {black triangles} is a subset of
{black cards}, we put {black triangles} ⊂ {black cards}.
Write out the subsets you found in 1.10 using this method.

1.12

Now make up {triangles} from your cards. Can you find any sub-sets in this set? Discuss your answers with your friends and with your teacher. Find out what the various triangles are called. Here are three of the subsets:

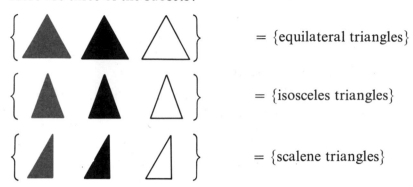

= {equilateral triangles}

= {isosceles triangles}

= {scalene triangles}

So we have:
{equilateral triangles} ⊂ {triangles}
{isosceles triangles} ⊂ {triangles}
{scalene triangles} ⊂ {triangles}.

1.13

Carry out a similar investigation on the following sets, writing down your results as in the example above.

(1) {quadrilaterals}   (2) {circles}.

1.14

All sets have subsets. Some have a lot of subsets, some a few, and one only one. Can you pick out a few of the subsets in the following sets? Write down your answers using the symbol ⊂ for subset.

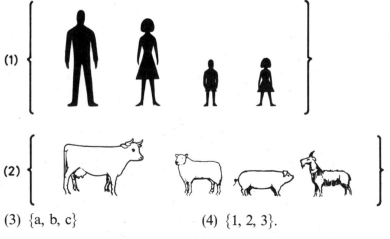

(1)

(2)

(3) {a, b, c}   (4) {1, 2, 3}.

4

Here are some examples of other sets and subsets:

$\{1, 2, 3, 4\} \subset \{$counting numbers$\}$

$\{$people in this form$\} \subset \{$people in this school$\}$

$\{$horses$\} \subset \{$animals$\}$

$\{$racing cars$\} \subset \{$cars$\}$.

Now make up at least five examples of your own, again using the symbol $\subset$ for 'is a subset of'.

1.16

Are the following subsets of the given sets?

(2) $\{$bowler, batsman, wicket-keeper$\} \subset \{$cricket players$\}$

(3) $\{$mice, hamsters, rabbits$\} \subset \{$pets$\}$

(4) $\{2, 4, 6, 8\} \subset \{1, 2, 3, 4, 5, 6\}$.

1.17

Take a card (a playing card or a piece of white card with the number 1 written on it). Using this card you can make two arrangements:

(1) leave it on the desk   (2) pick it up.

1.18

Now take two cards. With these you can make four arrangements:

(1) leave them both on the desk   (2) pick up one

(3) pick up the other   (4) pick up both.

1.19

Now take three cards and find out how many arrangements you can make. When you have done this, try four cards and then five cards. Record your results:

No. of cards	No. of arrangements
1	2
2	4
3	
4	
5	

1.20 Can you tell from your results how many arrangements can be
made with seven cards, eight cards, and ten cards? (Look for a
pattern in your results.)

1.20
In the last three paragraphs you have been finding out how many
subsets there are in a particular set. If you have {a, b, c} you can
tell from your work in 1.19 that, as there are three members of the
set, there will be eight subsets:
(1) {a, b, c}   (2) {a, b}   (3) {a, c}   (4) {b, c}ᐟ
(5) {a}   (6) {b}   (7) {c}   (8) { }.
The last one { } means an empty set or the set with no members.
This compares with leaving the cards on the desk.

1.21
Write down how many subsets there are in each of the following
sets and list the subsets as shown above. Playing cards will help you
with the first three.
(1) {Ace, King}   (2) {Ace, King, Queen}
(3) {Ace, King, Queen, Jack}   (4) {a, b}
(5) {1, 2, 3}   (6) {pink, blue}

1.22
Now return to your collection of shapes. Lay out {black cards} in
front of you. You saw that {black triangles} was a subset of
{black cards}. What was the symbol for subset? We can represent
this information by drawing a diagram. Mathematicians often find
it very helpful to draw diagrams or pictures to represent their work.
If we draw a shape like this ⬭ for {black cards} and a shape
like this △ for {black triangles} how can we put them together? Remember {black triangles} ⊂ {black cards}. Discuss your
ideas with your friends and your teacher.

1.23
Now draw diagrams to represent the following:
(1) {black quadrilaterals} ⊂ {black cards}
(2) {black circles} ⊂ {black cards}.

1.24
If we use ▭ to represent {blue cards} and △ to represent
{blue triangles} then we can draw the following diagram:

If we now shade in part of the diagram, which cards are represented by the shaded area?

1.25

(1) What statement does the following diagram represent if ☐ stands for {blue quadrilaterals}?

(2) What cards are represented by the shaded area in the following diagram?

1.26

Now look at the statement:

{King, Queen} ⊂ {Ace, King, Queen, Jack}.

We can draw this as follows:

Is the following statement true?

{Ace, King} ⊂ {Ace, King, Queen, Jack}.

If so, draw a diagram, and label the parts as above.

1.27

Are the following statements true? If so draw a diagram and label the parts as above.

(1) {King, Queen, Jack} ⊂ {Ace, King, Queen, Jack}

(2) {1, 2, 3} ⊂ {1, 2, 3, 4, 5, 6}

(3) {2, 5} ⊂ {1, 2, 3, 4}

(4) {John, Paul} ⊂ {John, Paul, George, Richard}

(5) {Paul, Richard} ⊂ {John, Paul, George, Richard}

(6) Draw one diagram to represent (4)–(5).

7

1.28 Recall

Where possible, name each of the following sets, remembering to use the curly brackets.

(1)

(2) {pear, orange, lemon, ———}
(3) {cabbage, peas, beans, sprouts, ———}
(4) {January, June, July}
(5) {fish, pink, sand, air}
(6) {tennis, cricket, football, hockey, ———}
(7) {hat, coat, skirt, ———}.

Look at the following sets; sort each set into subsets.

For example: {egg, bacon, sand, sausage, brick}.

Two subsets are:

{egg, bacon, sausage} ⊂ {things to eat}
{sand, brick} ⊂ {things with which to build}.

Now try these:

(8)

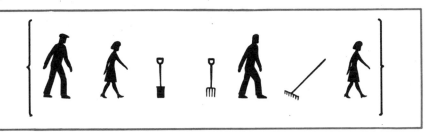

(9) {shoe, boat, slipper, yacht}

(10) {book, stool, newspaper, chair, comic, bench}.

Name at least three members of the following sets:

(11) {fish}   (12) {plants}

(13) {counties in England}   (14) {people who discovered America}.

Pick out at least one subset from each of the following sets.

Remember to use the symbol ⊂.

For example: {cup, saucer, plate, teapot}

{cup, plate} ⊂ {cup, saucer, plate, teapot}

(15) {1, 2, 3, 4}

(16) {star, moon, sun, planet}

(17) {raspberry, strawberry, gooseberry}

(18) {English, mathematics, history}.

Which of the following statements are true?

(19) {2, 4, 6} ⊂ {1, 2, 3, 4, 5, 6}

(20) {a, b} ⊂ {a, b, c}

(21) {pink, white} ⊂ {colours}

(22) {water, arsenic} ⊂ {things to drink}.

(23) Draw diagrams to illustrate your answers to (15) to (18).

(24) This diagram represents (19).

Fill in the numbers, putting each in its proper place. Then shade in the part which represents {2, 4, 6}.

(25) Do the same for (20) shading in the part representing {c}.

(26) This diagram represents (21). What does the shaded area represent?

1.29   By using any method you choose, find how many subsets there are in each of the following sets:

(28) {a, b, c}   (29) {1, 2, 3}.

1.29
Now return to your coloured shapes.

We have {triangles} as a subset of the first set and also of the second set. What other subsets are there in the first set? What other subsets are there in the second set?

1.30
Look at the following sets:

Name the two main subsets in each set. Are there any subsets which appear in both sets?

1.31

Now look at the following sets:

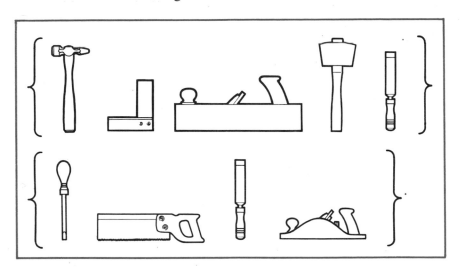

Name the sets and pick out any subsets. Are there any subsets which belong to both sets?

1.32

In each of the following look for any subsets which appear in both sets.

(2) {a, b, c, d, e}   {b, d, e, g, h}
(3) {1, 2, 3, 4, 5}   {2, 4, 6, 8, 10}
(4) {John, George, Paul, Richard}   {James, Cilla, Mary}.

1.33

To make it easier to talk about and write about sets, we often use capital letters to represent a set:

A = {birds}   B = {wild animals}.

We can then talk about set A or set B, or simply A or B.

1.34

Look again at 1.32 (1). First of all refer to it using capital letters:

$$A = \left\{ \text{◠ ◡ ◗} \right\}$$

$$B = \left\{ \text{◠ ⊔ ◡ ◡} \right\}$$

Can you draw a diagram to represent set A and set B? (Remember your previous work on drawing sets and subsets.)

If we let set A = ◯ᴬ and set B = ▭ᴮ, arrange the two shapes

to satisfy the sets. (Remember part of A is in part of B.) Discuss your results with your friends and your teacher.

1.35

Now take 1.32 (2) to (4) and draw them in diagram form.

1.36

When we have sets which overlap in this way we talk about the sets as intersecting or overlapping, for example:
If   A = {swallow, swift, lark, blackbird}   and
     B = {sparrow, thrush, robin, swift}.
These two sets overlap or intersect. The overlap or intersection is {swift}. We can represent these sets as shown in the diagram.

The shaded part is the
overlap or intersection
of the sets A and B.

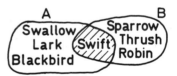

1.37

Now look at these two sets:

C = {London, Birmingham, Manchester}
D = {Newcastle, Cardiff, Glasgow, London}.

Do these two sets intersect? If so what is the intersection?
The intersection of these two sets is {London}.

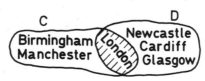

12

1.38

To avoid having to use the word intersection or overlap, we use the symbol ∩. Thus A ∩ B is read as 'the intersection of sets A and B' or simply 'A intersection B'.

1.39

If P = {1, 2, 3, 4, 5} and Q = {4, 5, 6, 7} the intersection or overlap of P and Q is {4, 5}, so we write: P ∩ Q = {4, 5} and draw:

1.40

Look at the following diagram which represents two sets, C and D.

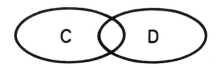

Shade in the portion of the diagram which represents C ∩ D. Check your results with your teacher.

1.41

(1)

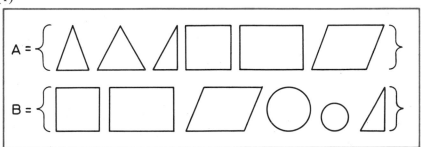

What is A ∩ B? Draw a diagram of your answer.
(2) C = {1, 2, 3, 4, 5, 6} and D = {2, 4, 6, 8, 10}.
What is C ∩ D? Draw a diagram and shade in C ∩ D. Fill in the numbers on your diagram.

1.41   Copy the following diagrams:

(3) (a) Shade in P ∩ Q.
    (b) Shade in B ∩ C.
    (c) Shade in all parts of sets A and B that are not in A ∩ B.
    (d) Shade in D ∩ E, F ∩ E, F ∩ D, and F ∩ D ∩ E.

(4) H = {a, b, c, d, e, f} and J = {c, g, e, h, f, o}. What is H ∩ J?
Draw a diagram and fill in the letters.

(5) A = {nail, hammer, chisel, saw} and
B = {plane, drill, wood, glue}.
What is A ∩ B?

(6) D = {days of the week} and E = {Monday, Tuesday, Wednesday, Thursday, Friday, Saturday, Sunday}.
What is D ∩ E? Draw a diagram of this.

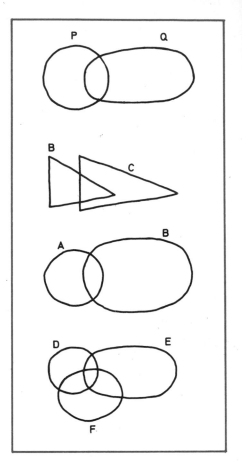

(7) The following diagram represents two sets of numbers:

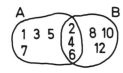

(a) Write out the members of set A and of set B.
(b) How many members are there in set A?
(c) How many members are there in set B?
(d) How many members are there in A ∩ B?
(e) How many members are there altogether? (Be careful with this last one.)
Note: we call the number of members in a set the *order* or *size* of the set. Thus set A is of order 7 and set B of order 6.

14

(8) The following diagram represents two sets of people:

(a) Write out the members of set P and of set Q.
(b) How many members are there in P ∩ Q?
(c) How many members are there altogether (be careful again)?
(d) What is the order of set P?
(e) What is the order of set Q?

1.42 Recall

Which of the following sets have elements with some common feature? Give names to those which have (don't forget to use { }).
(1) {French, German, English, Spanish, ---}
(2) {Cotton, wool, nylon, ---}
(3) {$\frac{1}{2}, \frac{2}{4}, \frac{3}{6}, \frac{4}{8}$, ---}   (4) {paint, James, red, fox}.
Name at least two subsets of the following sets. Don't forget to use the symbol for subset when writing out your answer.
(5) {w, x, y, z}   (6) {planets}
(7) {1, 2, 3}   (8) {forms in the school}
(9) {four-legged animals}   (10) {things that fly}.
How many subsets are there in the following sets?
(11) {1, 2}   (12) {p}
(13) {a, b, c}   (14) {Jack, Jill}.
Which of the following statements are true?
(15) {1, 2, 3} ⊂ {1, 2, 3, 4, 5, 6}
(16) {horse, bicycle} ⊂ {things to wear}
(17) {horse, bicycle} ⊂ {things to ride}.
Draw diagrams to represent the following statements and, where possible, label the diagrams.
(18) {June, July, August} ⊂ {months of the year}
(19) {Cowdrey, Sobers, Titmus} ⊂ {cricketers}.
(20) The following diagram represents two sets, P and Q.

(a) Is Q ⊂ P?
(b) How many members are there in set Q?
(c) How many members are there in set P?
(d) How many members are there altogether?
(e) How many members are there not in Q?
(f) What is the order of set P?
(g) What is the order of set Q?

15

(21) This diagram represents two sets, A and B. Is B a subset of A?

(22) A = {pupils who come to school by bus} and
     B = {pupils who stay for school dinner}. Find out to
which set or sets the members of your form belong.
Do any of the form belong to A ∩ B?
Now draw a diagram to represent these two sets.

(23) This diagram represents two sets, C and D.

You will remember that when sets overlap, as these do, we call it an intersection. What was the symbol for intersection?

(a) How many members are there in set C?
(b) How many members are there in set D?
(c) How many members are there in C ∩ D?
(d) How many members are there altogether?
(e) What is the order of set C?
(f) What is the order of set D?

(24)  Shade in A ∩ B.

(25) E = {whole numbers between 1 and 10} and
     F = {whole numbers between 7 and 12}.
(a) List the members of set E.
(b) List the members of set F.
(c) List the members of E ∩ F.

Interest page

Experiment 1

(1) On seven cards draw the following collections of shapes. Do not arrange them in an easily recognizable order.

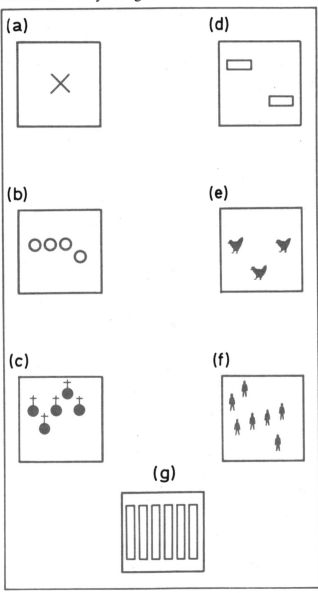

(2) Starting with the very simple collections and working up to the more difficult ones, show each of the cards to a friend, allowing him only a quick glance. Make a note of the largest number of objects that he can recognize, without counting. Repeat this experiment with more of your friends of different ages, and record your results.

Experiment 2

(1) Repeat the previous experiment with cards on which the objects are arranged in easily recognizable patterns.

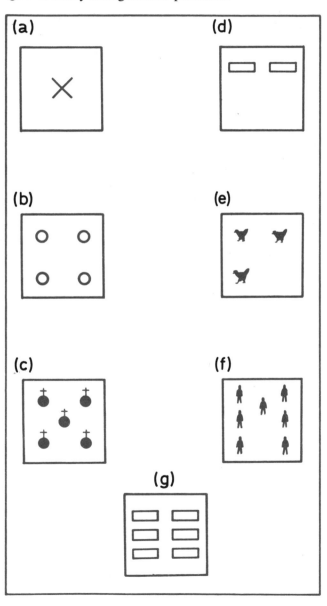

(2) Record your results, noting the highest number recognized in each case. Compare these results with those of the previous experiment.

(3) Is it easier to recognize numbers of objects in a group when they have been arranged in a pattern? Can you give any explanation of your answer? Arrangements like those shown in (b), (c), (f), and (g) of Experiment 2 can be found on playing cards and dominoes.

Further research

These experiments illustrate the need for a method of counting. Early man could not distinguish between numbers of objects greater than three or four, until he learnt to count. The early Aborigines of Tasmania had a counting system which consisted of {one, two, three, four, plenty}.

When man began to keep animals in flocks or herds, he had to keep a record of the number of animals in his possession, in order to ensure that none was lost.

Find out as much as you can about early methods of counting and the development of number systems. Compare each system with the others showing the advantages and disadvantages of each one.

Some books which may help you in your research are given below:

Number Systems, Old and New, Exploring Mathematics series, ed. J. Palframan (McGraw-Hill).

Man Must Measure, by Lancelot Hogben (Rathbone Books).

History of Number, by Thyra Smith (Basil Blackwell).

2. Number patterns

2.1
Copy the following and fill in the answers:
$$1 =$$
$$1 + 1 =$$
$$1 + 1 + 1 =$$
$$1 + 1 + 1 + 1 =$$
$$1 + 1 + 1 + 1 + 1 =$$
$$1 + 1 + 1 + 1 + 1 + 1 =$$
$$1 + 1 + 1 + 1 + 1 + 1 + 1 =$$

We have used the operation of addition to build up the set of whole numbers $\{1, 2, 3, 4, 5, ---\}$. Another name for this set is the set of *natural numbers*.

2.2
Using the set notation developed in chapter one, translate the following sentences into more mathematical language. The first one has been done for you.
(1) Two is a member of the set of natural numbers.
Answer: 2 is a member of {natural numbers}.
(2) Seven is an element of the set of natural numbers. (*Note:* 'is an element of' means the same as 'is a member of'.)
(3) Fifty-seven is a member of the set of natural numbers.
(4) Twelve thousand, seven hundred and fifty-six is an element of the set of natural numbers.
Mathematicians often use a symbol $\in$ to stand for 'is an element of' or 'is a member of'. It looks like the first letter of Element.
Two is a member of {natural numbers} can now be written: $2 \in$ {natural numbers}.
Richard is an element of the set of boys' names, now becomes Richard $\in$ {boys' names}.
How would you read Richard $\in$ {English Kings}?
(5) Answer (1) to (4) again, this time using the symbol $\in$.

2.3
Now look again at the set of natural numbers from 2.1. Using this set as a basis, write down the following new set: miss the first

element, write down the next (this is the first member of the new set), miss the next element, write down the next; repeat this procedure until you have five elements in your new set (the first two have been done for you): {2, 4, –––}.
(1) What name would you give this set?
(2) Is 12 ∈ {even numbers}?
(3) Is 15 ∈ {even numbers}?
(4) Is 20 ∈ {even numbers}?

2.4
Copy the following and fill in the answers:

$$2 =$$
$$2 + 2 =$$
$$2 + 2 + 2 =$$
$$2 + 2 + 2 + 2 =$$
$$2 + 2 + 2 + 2 + 2 =$$

Compare the set of answers that you get with the set of numbers you wrote down in 2.3.
We could refer to these answers as the two times table and write:

$$2 = 1 \times 2$$
$$2 + 2 = 2 \times 2$$
$$2 + 2 + 2 = 3 \times 2$$
$$2 + 2 + 2 + 2 = 4 \times 2$$
$$2 + 2 + 2 + 2 + 2 = 5 \times 2$$

Nobody likes doing unnecessary work and it does seem unnecessary to write down $2 + 2 + 2 + 2 + 2$ when in less than half the time we can write down 5×2.
Notice here that we have brought in a new operation: multiplication.

2.5
Now look at the right-hand side of the equations above. Each one of these answers (apart from the first and second) is a shorthand way of writing the left-hand side of the equation. We can shorten this even more; if we want to talk about the set of all these answers we give the answers a label which stands for this set and no other set. This label we call a *generalization*. Let us see if we can find this generalization by looking at the answers above. What factors are common to all of them?
There is a 2 in all of them, so a 2 must go in our generalization.
There is a '×' sign in all of them, so this also must go into our generalization.
Now, the next part looks a bit tricky. 1, 2, 3, 4, 5 are not the same elements, so that to use just *one* of them will not do. What have

these numbers in common? They are all elements of the set of natural numbers, so if we use N to stand for a natural number this can go into our generalization. Thus, we have for this set (i.e., the set of even numbers) the generalization $2 \times N$ which stands for *all even numbers*. We can shorten this even more by omitting the $\times$ sign and just writing 2N and agreeing to read this as two multiplied by N, where N is a natural number.

2.6
When N = 1   2N = 2   the first even number
When N = 2   2N = 4   the second even number
When N = 3   2N = 6   the third even number.
Write down the values of 2N in the following examples:
(1) N = 4   2N =   (2) N =   5   2N =
(3) N = 6   2N =   (4) N =   13   2N =
(5) N = 16   2N =   (6) N = 150   2N =
Note: as long as N is a natural number, 2N will always be an even number.
Generalization plays a very important part in mathematics and we must always be on the look out for a way of generalizing our results.

2.7
Let us look at one of our previous answers:
$$2 + 2 + 2 + 2 + 2 = 5 \times 2.$$
How would you describe the left-hand side of this equation? Can you see the very important link between the operation of addition and the operation of multiplication?

Multiplication is repeated addition.

A desk calculating machine uses this fact in order to multiply. For example, in order to multiply five by two it adds two five times (as in the left-hand side of the above equation) or it adds five twice as in the left-hand side of this equation: $5 + 5 = 2 \times 5$.

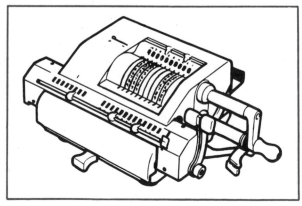

22

2.8

If we wanted to solve the following problems using a desk calculator, we could do it by one of two methods.

$4 \times 6 = 4 + 4 + 4 + 4 + 4 + 4 = 6 + 6 + 6 + 6$
        Add 4 six times   Add 6 four times.

$5 \times 12 = 5 + 5 + 5 + 5 + 5 + 5 + 5 + 5 + 5 + 5 + 5 + 5$
        Add 5 twelve times
       $= 12 + 12 + 12 + 12 + 12$
        Add 12 five times.

Which do you think is the easier method?

2.9

Write down two ways (for each problem) by which a desk calculating machine could solve the following multiplication problems by repeated addition:

(1) 6×5 (2) 5×7
(3) 3×11 (4) 6×3.

2.10

In 2.1 you wrote down a triangle of ones and added each line up; in doing so you built up the 'one times table' or the set of natural numbers. In 2.4 you wrote down a triangle of twos and built up the 'two times table' or the set of even numbers. You then went on to find a generalization for the set of even numbers, i.e., 2N where N is a generalization for the set of natural numbers.

Supposing we went on to write down a triangle of threes and added up each line.

(1) What would the resulting set of numbers be?
(2) What would the generalization for this set of numbers be?

2.11

The set of even numbers is a subset of the set of natural numbers. If we take the set of even numbers away from the set of natural numbers we are left with a new set of numbers; the set of *odd numbers*. Write down the set of odd numbers using the set brackets { }.

2.12

Translate the following statements fully into mathematical symbols.
(1) The set of even numbers is a subset of the set of natural numbers.
(2) The set of odd numbers is a subset of the set of natural numbers.

2.13

Copy the following and fill in the answers, stating to which set of numbers the answers belong.

(1) $2 - 1 =$ (2) $6 - 1 =$
(3) $10 - 1 =$ (4) $36 - 1 =$
(5) $68 - 1 =$ (6) $206 - 1 =$

Did you notice that in every case by subtracting 1 from an even number the answer is an odd number? Thus we can write:

an even number $- 1 =$ an odd number.

You have already found a generalization for an even number. Can you find a generalization for an odd number from the above equation? If instead of an even number we write down 2N (which is the generalization for an even number) in the above equation, we have: $2N - 1 =$ an odd number.

And this gives us our generalization for an odd number: $2N - 1$.

2.14

When $N = 1$ $2N - 1 = 1$ the first odd number
When $N = 2$ $2N - 1 = 3$ the second odd number
When $N = 3$ $2N - 1 = 5$ the third odd number.

Write down the values of $2N - 1$ in the following examples:

(1) $N = 7$ $2N - 1 =$ (2) $N = 8$ $2N - 1 =$
(3) $N = 9$ $2N - 1 =$ (4) $N = 12$ $2N - 1 =$

(Remember N can be any natural number.)

2.15

What kind of number does the generalization $2N + 1$ stand for?
When $N = 1$ then $2N + 1 = 3$
When $N = 2$ then $2N + 1 = 5$
When $N = 3$ then $2N + 1 = 7$.

Are there any odd numbers that we cannot get from the generalization $2N + 1$ where N is a natural number?

2.16

Copy the following equations and fill in the gaps:

(1) $2 + 4 =$ (2) $32 + 4 =$
(3) $+ 12 = 22$ (4) $+ 6 = 20$
(5) $2 +$ $= 50$ (6) $6 +$ $= 24$.

The numbers in all of these equations have something in common. They are all even numbers. From the equations above we can say that: an even number + an even number = an even number.
Is this always true?

Copy the following and fill in the gaps. Use your answers to
enable you to complete the final equations.

(1) 2 +   = 5   (2)   6 + 3 =
(3) 10 +   = 15   (4) 20 +   = 51
(5)   8 + 13 =   (6) 90 +   = 95

          an even number + an odd number =

(7)   3 + 10 =   (8)   7 +   = 121
(9) 61 + 6 =   (10)   + 10 =   31
(11) 61 +   = 121   (12) 13 + 20 =

          an odd number + an even number =

(13)   3 + 5 =   (14) 17 + 11 =
(15)   + 19 = 30   (16)   + 9 = 20
(17)   3 + 7 =   (18)   5 + 21 =

          an odd number + an odd number =

One of the oldest games in the world is the game of odds and evens.
It was an ancient game even in Plato's day. Over the ages vast
amounts of money have changed hands because of this game. The
rules of play are:

One player holds a number of coins or objects in his closed hand
while another player tries to guess whether the coins (or objects) are
even or odd in number.

2.18

Copy the following and fill in the answers:

$$1 =$$
$$2 + 1 =$$
$$3 + 2 + 1 =$$
$$4 + 3 + 2 + 1 =$$
$$5 + 4 + 3 + 2 + 1 =$$

The numbers 1, 3, 6, 10, 15, — — — were of great importance to the
Greeks, mainly because these numbers are related to geometric
shapes. They are known as the *triangular numbers*. There is a reason
for this. If we write down a dot for every unit in the number we can
arrange the dots in the following way:

        1
        3
        6
        10

Now can you see why these numbers are called triangular numbers?

2.19

(2.19 to 2.21 inclusive are optional.)

Because they follow a pattern, it would suggest that there must be a generalization for triangular numbers. Look again at the way in which they are built up:

$$1 = 1 \qquad \text{the first triangular number}$$
$$2 + 1 = 2 + (2 - 1) \qquad \text{the second triangular number}$$
$$3 + 2 + 1 = 3 + (3 - 1) + (3 - 2)$$
$$\text{the third triangular number}$$
$$4 + 3 + 2 + 1 = 4 + (4 - 1) + (4 - 2) + (4 - 3)$$
$$\text{the fourth triangular number}$$
$$5 + 4 + 3 + 2 + 1 = 5 + (5 - 1) + (5 - 2) + (5 - 3) + (5 - 4)$$
$$\text{the fifth triangular number.}$$

These are all natural numbers. If we want to build up a triangular number, we start with a natural number (N) and add to it $(N - 1)$, $(N - 2)$, $(N - 3)$, and so on until we reach 1. Thus we have a generalization of a triangular number as:

$$N + (N - 1) + (N - 2) + (N - 3) + (N - 4) + --- + 1.$$

There is another (and simpler) generalization for a triangular number which you will meet later.

2.20

If $N = 8$ we have the eighth triangular number:

$$8 + (8 - 1) + (8 - 2) + (8 - 3) + (8 - 4) + (8 - 5) + (8 - 6) + (8 - 7)$$

Work this out and draw the triangle of dots that represents it.

2.21

For the triangular number ten we have $N = 4$. Putting this in the generalization for a triangular number we have:

$$4 + (4 - 1) + (4 - 2) + (4 - 3) = 10$$
$$4 + \quad 3 \quad + \quad 2 \quad + \quad 1 \quad = 10$$

In the generalization for a triangular number, what would N have to equal for the following triangular numbers?

(1) triangular number 3   (2) triangular number 6
(3) triangular number 15   (4) triangular number 21.

2.22

Compile a list, using set notation, of the first twenty triangular numbers.

(1) What is the eighteenth triangular number?
(2) What is the eleventh triangular number?
(3) What is the fifteenth triangular number?

2.24
Copy the following and fill in the answers:

$$1 =$$
$$3 + 1 =$$
$$5 + 3 + 1 =$$
$$7 + 5 + 3 + 1 =$$
$$9 + 7 + 5 + 3 + 1 =$$
$$11 + 9 + 7 + 5 + 3 + 1 =$$
$$13 + 11 + 9 + 7 + 5 + 3 + 1 =$$

The answers to these questions all have something in common, i.e., they are all elements of the set of *square numbers*. These square numbers can be represented in a similar way to the triangular numbers:

Number of dots in side of square

$1 = 1 \times 1$ 1

$4 = 2 \times 2$ 2

$9 = 3 \times 3$ 3

$16 = 4 \times 4$ 4

$25 = 5 \times 5$ 5

$36 = 6 \times 6$ 6

Hence the name square numbers.

2.25
How many dots form the side of the square array for the following square numbers?
(1) The square number 4   (2) The square number 9

(3) The square number 16   (4) The square number 25
(5) The square number 36   (6) The square number 144.

2.26
Is there a quick way of finding how many dots there are in the whole diagram of a square number, without counting them all?

2.27
Use this method to say what square number the following array of dots stands for:

2.28
Compile a list, using set notation, of the first fifteen square numbers.

2.29
(1) What is the thirteenth square number?
(2) What is the ninth square number?
(3) What is the tenth square number?
Look again at the figures which you wrote down in 2.24.
Now let us compare the first column with the third column.
For the first square number (1) *1* is multiplied by itself and this is equal to the *first* odd number.
For the second square number (4) *2* is multiplied by itself and this equals the sum of the first *two* odd numbers.

28

For the third square number (9) *3* is multiplied by itself and this equals the sum of the first *three* odd numbers, etc.

Thus we have two methods of finding these square numbers.

If we want to find the sixth square number (36) we could: (a) add the first six odd numbers, or (b) multiply six by six.

We found earlier that a desk calculating machine cannot multiply. It performs multiplication by a process of repeated addition. So, if we wanted to work out the sixth square number with a calculating machine, we would have to (a) add the first six odd numbers or (b) add six, six times.

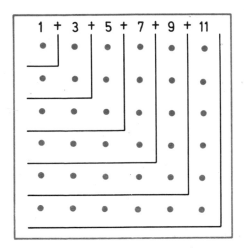

2.30

Work out the eighteenth square number by the addition of odd numbers (i.e., method (a) of the calculating machine).

2.31

If you have a desk calculating machine, use it to find the thirty-second square number.

2.32

Look at the square number arrays again:

1

4

9

16

2.33
From these diagrams you can see that square numbers can be split up into triangular numbers. The square number four can be expressed as the sum of the triangular numbers one and three, thus: $4 = 3 + 1$.

Express the following square numbers as sums of triangular numbers:

(1) 9   (2) 16   (3) 25

(4) 36   (5) 49   (6) 64

Thus the square numbers can be expressed as (a) the sums of odd numbers or (b) the sums of triangular numbers.

2.33
Write down, in set notation, the set of numbers whose generalization is 2N. (Remember your previous work.)

What is the name of this set of numbers?

Another name for this set of numbers is the set of *multiples of 2*. All the numbers in this set can be divided by 2.

The set of numbers {3, 6, 9, 12, 15, 18, 21, 24, ---} is the set of *multiples of 3*. The generalization for this set of numbers is 3N.

When   N = 1   3N = 3   the first element in the set

When   N = 2   3N = 6   the second element in the set

When   N = 3   3N = 9   the third element in the set

When   N = 4   3N = 12   the fourth element in the set

When   N = 10   3N = 30   the tenth element in the set.

Which of the following statements are true?

(1) $15 \in \{$multiples of 3$\}$

(2) $19 \in \{$multiples of 3$\}$

(3) $36 \in \{$multiples of 3$\}$.

2.34
(1) Write down the generalization for the set of multiples of 4.

(2) Write down the set of multiples of 4 using set notation.

2.35
Copy the following and fill in the first five members of each of the sets given and the generalization:

(1) the set of multiples of 5   (2) the set of multiples of 6

(3) the set of multiples of 7   (4) the set of multiples of 9

(5) the set of multiples of 10   (6) the set of multiples of 30.

The generalization	The set
(1)	
(2)	
(3)	
(4)	
(5)	
(6)	

There are some numbers which are elements of more than one of the sets of multiples, for example, 12 is an element of the set of multiples of 2, 3, 4, 6, and 12 or in set notation:

$$12 \in \{2, 4, 6, 8, 10, 12, 14, ---\}$$
$$12 \in \{3, 6, 9, 12, 15, ---\}$$
$$12 \in \{4, 8, 12, 16, 20, 24, ---\}$$
$$12 \in \{6, 12, 18, 24, 30, ---\}$$
$$12 \in \{12, 24, 36, 48, ---\}.$$

2.36
Write down, using set notation, the sets of multiples to which the following numbers belong:
(1) 10　　　(2) 6　　　(3) 8　　　(4) 15
(5) 120　　(6) 2　　　(7) 13　　(8) 7.
From the above examples, we can say of the numbers 10, 6, 8, and 15 that:

10 is a multiple of 2, 5, and 10
6 is a multiple of 2, 3, and 6
8 is a multiple of 2, 4, and 8
15 is a multiple of 3, 5, and 15.

2.37
Complete the following statements:
(1) 20 is a multiple of　　　(2) 30 is a multiple of
(3) 40 is a multiple of　　　(4) 50 is a multiple of
(5) 66 is a multiple of　　　(6) 120 is a multiple of

2.38
There is a very special set of multiples, i.e., the set of multiples whose generalization is N. (We have met this set before.) This is the set of multiples of 1. Write it down using set notation.

All the natural numbers belong to the set of multiples of 1; so to be mathematically correct we must modify our statement and write:

10 is a multiple of 1, 2, 5, and 10
6 is a multiple of 1, 2, 3, and 6
8 is a multiple of 1, 2, 4, and 8
15 is a multiple of 1, 3, 5, and 15.

Modify the statements that you made in 2.37.

2.39

In 2.36 the numbers 2, 13, and 7 each belong to only two sets of multiples, i.e., their own set of multiples and the set of multiples of 1. For example:

2 is a multiple of 1 and 2
13 is a multiple of 1 and 13
7 is a multiple of 1 and 7.

Can you find any other numbers less than twenty for which this is true?

Since these numbers are different from the others and have something in common, they belong to a special set of numbers, the set of *prime numbers*.

It is prime numbers that set mathematicians one of their most baffling problems, for try as they might, the great mathematicians have never been able to find a generalization for a prime number. A Greek mathematician by the name of Eratosthenes worked out a method of finding prime numbers by writing down the natural numbers and cancelling the elements of the sets of multiples except the first number. This is known as the *Sieve of Eratosthenes*

1	2	3	4	5	6	7	8	9	10
11	12	13	14	15	16	17	18	19	20
21	22	23	24	25	26	27	28	29	30
31	32	33	34	35	36	37	38	39	40
41	42	43	44	45	46	47	48	49	50
51	52	53	54	55	56	57	58	59	60
61	62	63	64	65	66	67	68	69	70
71	72	73	74	75	76	77	78	79	80
81	82	83	84	85	86	87	88	89	90
91	92	93	94	95	96	97	98	99	100

2.40

Copy this table of numbers and use Eratosthenes' method to find the set of prime numbers between 1 and 100.
The cancelling of the set of multiples of 2 has been started for you;

all you have to do is finish the cancelling of these multiples and then
continue by cancelling the sets of multiples of 3, 4, 5, 6, ---, etc.,
until you are sure that the only numbers that are left are prime
numbers. Remember that you leave the first member of a set of
multiples and start your cancelling with the second member, unless
the first has already been cancelled.

2.41
Now look at the following:

$1 = 1 \times 1$	$8 = 1 \times 2 \times 2 \times 2$
$2 = 1 \times 2$	$9 = 1 \times 3 \times 3$
$3 = 1 \times 3$	$10 = 1 \times 2 \times 5$
$4 = 1 \times 2 \times 2$	$11 = 1 \times 11$
$5 = 1 \times 5$	$12 = 1 \times 2 \times 2 \times 3$
$6 = 1 \times 2 \times 3$	$13 = 1 \times 13$
$7 = 1 \times 7$	$14 = 1 \times 2 \times 7$

All the natural numbers can be expressed as the *product* of prime
numbers.

2.42
Express the following numbers as products of prime numbers:
(1)   15   (2)   16   (3)   20   (4)   25
(5)   36   (6)   45   (7)   100   (8)   124
(9)   125   (10) 169   (11) 300   (12) 560.

2.43 Recall
(1) Find the sum of:
(a) the first four odd numbers   (b) the first six odd numbers
(c) the first seven odd numbers   (d) the first ten odd numbers.
(2) The answers to (1) are *all* elements of two sets, give the two
sets.
(3) Write down the generalization for an even number and use it
to find:
(a) the tenth member of the set of even numbers
(b) the fourteenth member of the set of even numbers
(c) the thirty-first member of the set of even numbers.
(4) In the set of natural numbers, the first odd number is one less
than the first even number, the second odd number is one less than
the second even number, the third odd number is one less than the
third even number, and so on. Write down the generalizations for
an odd number and an even number and explain how these
generalizations indicate this fact.
(5) The sixteenth even number is 32. What is the sixteenth odd
number?

(6) The twentieth even number is 40. What is the twentieth odd number? What is the twenty-first odd number?

(7) The fifteenth odd number is 29. What is the fifteenth even number? What is the fourteenth even number?

(8) Find the sum of:

(a) the first three natural numbers

(b) the first five natural numbers

(c) the first nine natural numbers

(d) the first ten natural numbers.

(9) The answers to (8) are *all* elements of two sets, give the two sets.

(10) Write down the generalization for a square number and use it to find:

(a) the seventh square number   (b) the tenth square number

(c) the twelfth square number   (d) the thirteenth square number.

(11) Find the sum of:

(a) the first seven odd numbers   (b) the first twelve odd numbers.

(12) The answers to (10) and (11) are *all* elements of two sets, give the two sets.

(13) {Prime numbers} $\subset$ {natural numbers}. Give four more examples of a set and subset that you have met in this chapter. Write your answers in set notation.

(14) Translate the following mathematical notations into words:

(a) $3 \in \{1, 2, 3, 4, 5, 6, 7, 8, 9, 10, ---\}$

(b) $3 \in \{1, 3, 5, 7, 9, 11, 13, 15, 17, ---\}$

(c) $9 \in \{1, 4, 9, 16, 25, 36, 49, 64, 81, 100, ---\}$

(d) $\{1, 4, 9, 16, 25, 36, 49, 64, 81, 100, ---\}$
$\subset \{1, 2, 3, 4, 5, 6, 7, 8, ---\}$

(15) Write down three sets of numbers of which 6 is an element.

(16) 6 also belongs to the set of *perfect numbers*. The numbers 1, 2, and 3 are the only natural numbers that will divide into 6 exactly (apart from 6 itself) and $6 = 1 + 2 + 3$. This is why 6 is said to be perfect.

6 is the first perfect number; the third perfect number is 496, because the only natural numbers that will divide exactly into 496 (other than 496 itself) are 1, 2, 4, 8, 16, 31, 62, 124, and 248.

$1 + 2 + 4 + 8 + 16 + 31 + 62 + 124 + 248 = 496$.

Can you find the second perfect number? It lies between 20 and 30. [The fourth perfect number is 8,128 and the fifth perfect number is 33,550,336. These can be checked on a desk calculator. *Note:* all of the perfect numbers are elements of the set of natural numbers.]

(17) The intersection between the set of even numbers and the set of prime numbers contains only one element: 2. Why is 2 the only even prime number?

Interest page

Experiment 1
(1) On a sheet of paper, use a penny to draw nine circles and number the circles from one to nine. On the circumference of the first circle mark two points; space your points out as equally as possible. On the circumference of the second circle, mark three points, equally spaced. On the third, mark four points, and so on, to the ninth circle which should have ten equally spaced points on its circumference.
(2) In each circle, join every point on the circumference to every other point using straight lines only. This is the greatest possible number of ways of joining up the points on the circumference.
(3) In each case count the number of lines joining the points. Copy and complete the following table:

Number of points	Greatest number of possible lines joining these points
2	
3	
4	
5	
6	
7	
8	
9	
10	

(4) Look at the numbers in the second column. To which set of numbers do they belong?
(5) Prepare material for display on this topic. Some of the patterns obtained are worth looking at. For example, the following drawing shows the greatest possible number of lines joining eighteen equally spaced points on the circumference of a circle. The greatest number of possible lines in this case is 153.

Experiment 2

The following diagram shows the patterns formed by the set of multiples of 3 on the hundred square.

1	2	3	4	5	6	7	8	9	10
11	12	13	14	15	16	17	18	19	20
21	22	23	24	25	26	27	28	29	30
31	32	33	34	35	36	37	38	39	40
41	42	43	44	45	46	47	48	49	50
51	52	53	54	55	56	57	58	59	60
61	62	63	64	65	66	67	68	69	70
71	72	73	74	75	76	77	78	79	80
81	82	83	84	85	86	87	88	89	90
91	92	93	94	95	96	97	98	99	100

$$\{3, 6, 9, 12, 15, --\!-, 99, --\!-, 3N\}$$

On several hundred squares of your own, draw the patterns formed
by other sets of numbers. For example, you could draw the patterns
for the sets of multiples of 4, 5, 6, etc., or the set of even numbers,
square numbers, triangular numbers, etc. With some sets of numbers
the patterns are not as obvious as they are for the set above.

Experiment 3

Here are some examples of how number patterns can be shown in a
different way.

The set of odd numbers:

		o	o	o	o	o
	o	oo	ooo	oooo	ooooo	oooooo
o	oo	oo	ooo	oooo	ooooo	oooooo
1	3	5	7	9	11	13

The set of even numbers (or multiples of 2):

	oo	ooo	oooo	ooooo	oooooo	ooooooo
oo	oo	ooo	oooo	ooooo	oooooo	ooooooo
2	4	6	8	10	12	14

The set of multiples of 3:

						ooo
					ooo	ooo
				ooo	ooo	ooo
			ooo	ooo	ooo	ooo
		ooo	ooo	ooo	ooo	ooo
	ooo	ooo	ooo	ooo	ooo	ooo
ooo	ooo	ooo	ooo	ooo	ooo	ooo
3	6	9	12	15	18	21

Try this technique with the set of multiples of 4, 5, 6, etc. You have
already seen this method used for the set of triangular numbers and
the set of square numbers.

3. About shape

Materials required
A supply of paper, preferably plain; a pair of scissors; a ruler;
compasses; and pencils.

3.1
Take a sheet of paper and fold it in half. Starting from the folded
edge cut out any shape you wish. Can you say what your shape will
look like when you open it out? Make a rough sketch of what you
think the result will be.
Open out your shape and check it with your sketch. What can you
say about the opened out shape? Is it the same on either side of the
crease? Yes; one side is a reflection of the other. Why do we
use the word reflection? Will this be the case for every shape you
cut? Cut out other shapes and see if you can find an example where
one side is not a reflection of the other.
Compare your results with your friends'.

3.2
Use the folding and cutting method to produce the following
shapes:

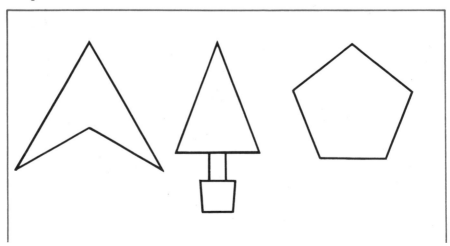

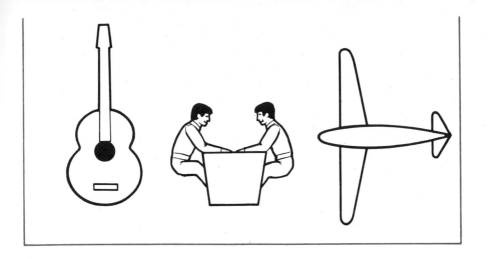

3.3
Now invent some designs of your own.

3.4
When we have shapes such as the ones we have been looking at,
i.e., shapes which are the same (or reflected) on either side of a
centre line, we say that the shapes are *symmetrical about a line*.
We shall see in the next few pages that many things in our lives,
both natural and man-made, are symmetrical about a line.

3.5
Take a fresh sheet of paper, fold it in half and mark on it the shape
shown.

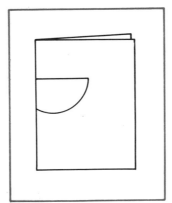

What will you get on cutting out this shape? Make a sketch of what
you think your result will be. Cut out the shape and see if you were
right.
You should have a letter **B**.

3.6

Can you produce the number **8** in a similar way? There are two possible ways of producing the number **8**. Can you find the second?

3.7

Now investigate all of the capital letters and all of the numbers from 0 to 9 to find which are symmetrical about a line. Make up a wall chart of your results and record them neatly in your book, marking in all lines of symmetry.

3.8

Look around the classroom and make a list of at least twelve items that are symmetrical. Have you, or your clothes, or any of your belongings, any lines of symmetry? Make a list of any such items with sketches to show the lines of symmetry.

3.9

What about outside the classroom? What sort of things in nature have lines of symmetry? Let us start by looking at the insect world. Have the following insects any lines of symmetry?

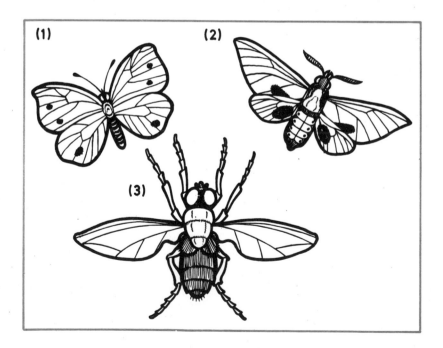

Trace the above pictures, colour them, and draw in the lines of symmetry.

Look at the following pictures of birds, animals, plants. Have any
of these any lines of symmetry?

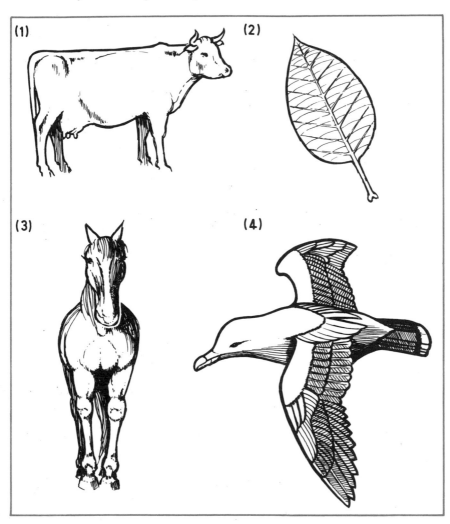

Trace the above pictures, colour them, and draw in the lines of
symmetry.
Prepare large, coloured wall charts of the above and also of any
other creatures and plants that have lines of symmetry. The simplest
ways of doing this are by tracing examples from books and collecting specimens.

3.11

Finally, let us look at drawings of man-made things. You should
already have a list of man-made things in the classroom which have
lines of symmetry. Have the following any lines of symmetry?

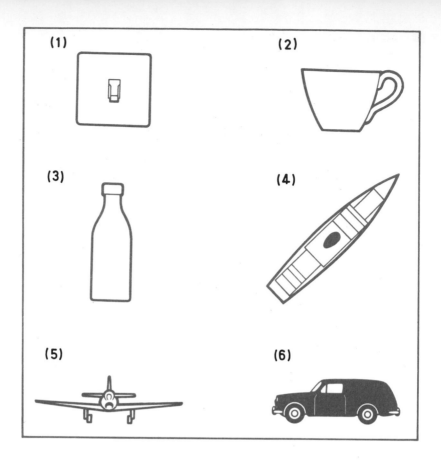

(1) **(2)** **(3)** **(4)** **(5)** **(6)**

3.12

Now, let us consider mathematical shapes.

(1) The *rectangle*
In how many ways can you cut a rectangle from a folded piece of paper? Record your results.

(2) The *square*
In how many ways can you cut a square from a folded piece of paper? Record your results.

(3) The *triangle*
In how many ways can you cut triangles from a folded piece of paper? Be careful here for there are three different types of triangle. Record your results.

3.13

Take each of the shapes in 3.12 and letter them as shown:

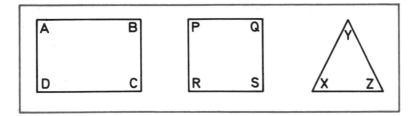

Now, taking the rectangle first, you should have found that you could cut it out in two ways. In how many ways can you put it back in the hole? (The answer is not two.)
In how many ways can the square be put back? (The answer is not four.)
In how many ways can the triangles be put back?
Record your results.

3.14
Copy the following table and complete it:

Shape	No. of lines of symmetry	No. of ways of putting back	Where found in real life
Rectangle Square Triangle Triangle Triangle			

3.15
(1) Name three members of the following sets which have lines of symmetry:
A = {letters of the alphabet}   B = {cutlery}
C = {numbers less than 10}   D = {furniture}.

(2) How many lines of symmetry have the following items?
(a) a motor car   (b) a book
(c) a frying pan   (d) a coin
(e) a tea cup   (f) a fish.

3.16
Cut a rectangle from a piece of paper. Fold the rectangle in half, then in half again, and finally in half again.

3.17   How many thicknesses of paper have you?
Open out your sheet of paper; you should have:

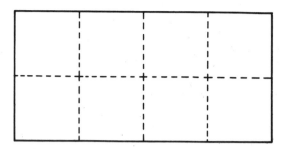

The surface of the original rectangle is covered with smaller rectangles. How many small rectangles are there?
(1) How many rectangles can you find in the above diagram (there
are more than twenty)?
(2) To produce the above rectangle you folded the paper three
times. Start with a fresh rectangle, as large as you like, and fold it as
you did above. Now fold it in half again, and again, and again, until
you cannot fold it any more. Try this with rectangles of different
sizes and see what is the largest number of folds you can make

3.17
Take another rectangle and fold it in half and in half again.

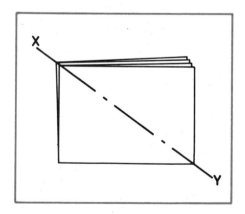

Now fold along line XY.
Crease firmly.
Can you say how many thicknesses of paper there are?
What shape will the rectangle be divided into?
Open out your paper, you should have:

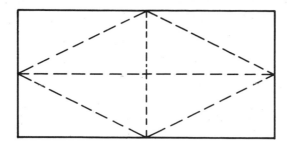

This time the surface is covered with triangles.
How many triangles can you find?

3.18
You have seen that it is possible to cover a surface with certain shapes. So far we have considered triangles and rectangles. Look at the floor of your classroom. What shapes have been used in making the floor? Make a sketch of the pattern on your classroom floor. Are there any fancy patterns near the edges of the floor?
During break or lunchtime, go around the school and sketch all the different floor or wall patterns you can find. Do the same at home. When you have a good collection of patterns, find out how many different shapes have been used. Make wall charts of your results.

3.19
Now try designing some patterns of your own.
Work in twos or threes.
First cut out ten triangles as shown below. Use the paper folding method.

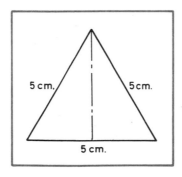

Now try to fit the ten triangles together to form attractive patterns.

3.20   Here is an example to help you:

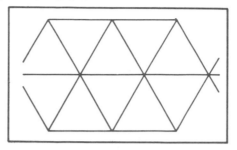

Make a sketch of each pattern you produce and colour your sketches.

3.20

Next cut out ten triangles as shown below. Again use the paper folding method.

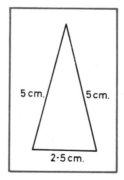

Using the triangles of 3.19 and those you have just made, see what new patterns you can create.

Here is an example to help you:

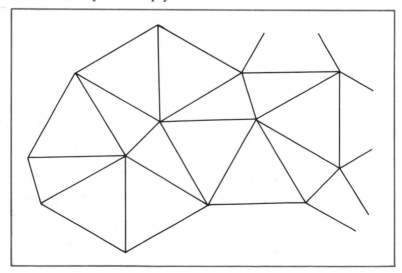

Make a sketch of each pattern you produce and colour your
sketches.

3.21
Finally, cut out ten squares with sides 2·5 *cm* long. Again use the
paper folding method.
Using these squares and the triangles of 3.19 and 3.20, design some
new patterns.
Make a sketch of each pattern you produce and colour your
sketches.

3.22
Make up wall charts in full colour of your best patterns.
A famous Dutch artist, Maurit L. Esher, who lives in Bourn, has
produced many beautiful paintings based on shape patterns (or
tessellations as mathematicians call them). He uses more complex
shapes than those which you have been using. Try to find some
examples of his work.
Would you like to produce paintings like those of Esher? During
this course we shall study tessellations in greater detail so that you
may well be able to design some more complex ones of your own.
To help you on your way, this little chicken can be made from
coloured card and then fitted into an attractive picture.

Trace the chicken carefully and transfer the tracing to the coloured
card. Cut out between six and twelve chickens and then fit them
together to produce a picture. Stick the chickens on to a sheet of
paper and hang up your picture.
You could of course use plain card and paint your picture after-
wards.

3.23

You may be wondering what all this pattern work has to do with mathematics. Well, to quote a famous English mathematician, G. H. Hardy, 'A mathematician like a painter or poet is a maker of patterns.' That is, mathematics is concerned with patterns, either the study of them or the discovery of them. In chapter two you studied number patterns, here we have been looking at shape patterns, and in future chapters we shall be looking at other patterns.

3.24

(1) Sketch the following patterns. Can you now continue them?

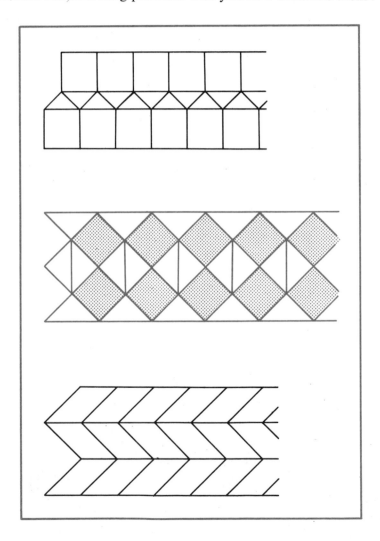

(2) Make up some patterns from the following shapes:

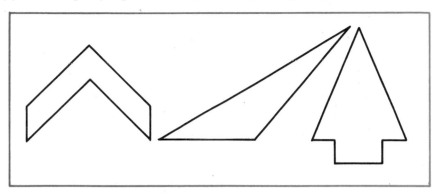

3.25

There are a number of interesting patterns which you can produce and which are very different from the ones you have just been doing. Begin by drawing two lines as shown:

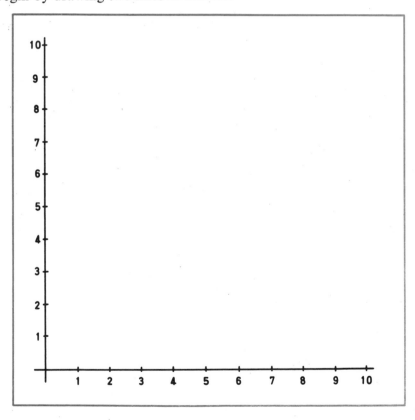

Mark each line at one centimetre intervals.
Join point 10 on the vertical line to point 1 on the horizontal line.
Join 9 to 2, 8 to 3, 7 to 4, 6 to 5, and so on.

3.26   When you have finished you should get something like this:

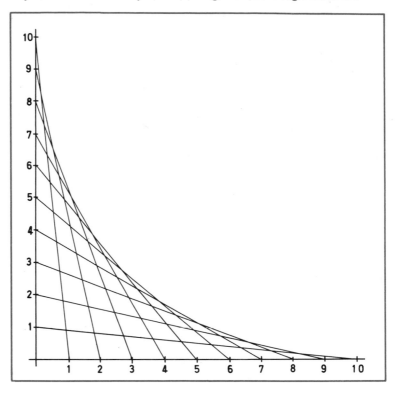

You have used straight lines to produce a curved pattern.

3.26
Repeat your work of 3.25, but draw the two starting lines like this:

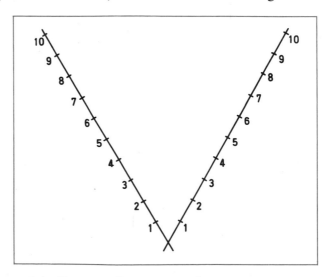

Do these straight lines produce a curved pattern?

Use a whole page to draw the following:

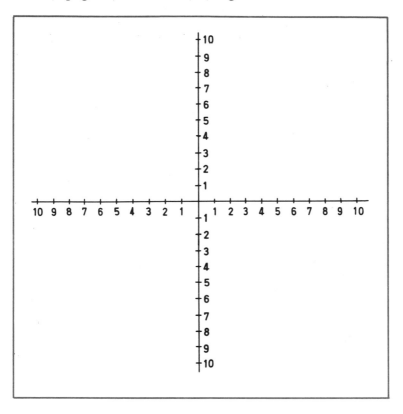

Mark the lines in one centimetre steps and repeat the work of 3.25 in each part of the diagram. (Make sure you have the same number of steps vertically as you have horizontally.)

3.28

Now design some patterns of your own. Here is an example to help you:

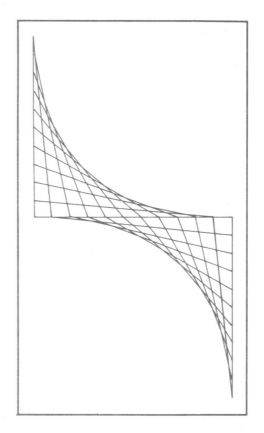

3.29

An interesting variation of the above work is to produce these patterns, not by drawing, but by using pieces of coloured silk or wool. To do this you need pieces of white card about 15 *cm* by 15 *cm*. On the card draw two lines as shown in 3.25.

Mark the lines at 1 *cm* intervals. Make a small hole through each mark using a compass point. Thread your coloured silk or wool (embroidery silks are the best as the colours are much brighter) through a darning needle or large sewing needle, tie a knot in the end of the silk, and you are ready to start.

Hold the card in front of you with one hand and the needle and silk in the other, pass the needle through hole 10 from the back of the card. Pull the silk until the knot rests against the back of the card. Now pass the needle down through hole 1 and pull the silk tight. Next, pass the needle up through hole 2, on across to hole 9, and pull tight.

Pass the needle up through hole 8 and down through hole 3. Then up through hole 4 and down through hole 7, and so on until the pattern is complete.

Remember that if you go down through one hole you should come up through the next hole. This saves wasting your wool or silk.

3.30

You can produce all the patterns in 3.25, 3.26, 3.27, and 3.28, plus many more, by this method.

A curve formed in this way is called an envelope.

To give you some more ideas, read the booklet, *Curve Stitching* by A. E. James, Topics for Modern Schools series (Oxford University Press).

Interest page

The art of origami

In the early part of this chapter we used the paper folding method to make shapes such as butterflies, moths, triangles, rectangles, etc. The art of producing paper shapes, or origami as it is called, goes back many centuries. It has always been a favourite pastime of the Japanese. It has become popular in the western world during the last fifty years.

There are hundreds of shapes, from fish to elephants, from flowers to palm trees, that can be produced by folding squares or triangles of paper. A number of the models produced can also be made to work, such as a flapping bird or a jumping frog.

As an introduction to this fascinating subject try making the model which is described below.

House (Traditional Japanese)

(1) Fold the top and bottom edges to the centre at the back.

(2) Fold the right and left edges to the centre in front.

(3) Pull the two upper corners outward and flatten them into the position shown in (4).

(4) The courtyard is now facing you. Turn the model over.

(5) The house is now seen from the front.

Further research

Find out all you can about origami work. Two books which should prove most helpful are *The Art of Origami* and *The Best of Origami*. Both are written by Samuel Randlett and published by Faber and Faber.

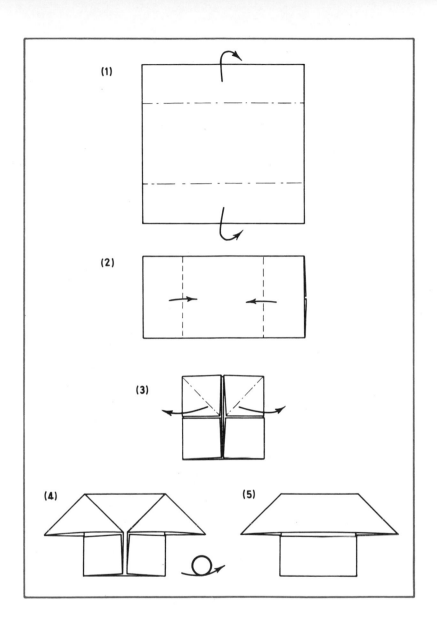

4. About size

4.1

How big? How small? What size? Which is the largest? Which is the smallest? We use these and many similar expressions every day of our lives. In this chapter we are going to take a look at these expressions to see just what they mean and how a mathematician makes use of them.

How good are you at sorting out which things are largest or 4.2
smallest? Below are eight sets of things; go through each set carefully and say which is the largest and which is the smallest member
of each set.

(1)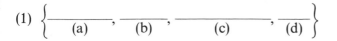

(2) {elephant, lion, dog}

(3)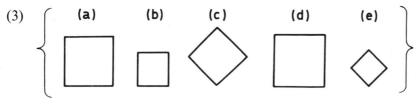

(4) {74, 63, 47, 36, 81, 29, 92, 67, 76}
(5) {Pupils in your form}
(6) {Members of your family}
(7) {99 *g*, 2 *kg*, 30 *g*, 1 *kg*}
(8) {£1·10. £1·00, 50*p*, 35*p*}.

4.2
In each of the following can you say, by looking only, which is the
longest line or largest shape?

(1)

(2)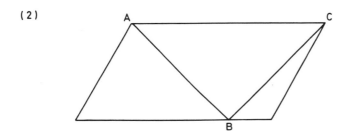

4.3
If we have {horse, elephant, dog, mouse, rabbit}, which is the
largest animal? Which is next in size? Which next? Which next?
Which is the smallest?

4.4 Write down the set again putting the animals in order, largest first. Answer the above questions for each of the following sets and rewrite the sets putting the members in order, largest first.
(1) {cat, lion, goat, cow, giraffe}   (2) {3, 11, 7, 21, 6, 4, 19}
(3) {newt, cod, whale, shark}   (4) {6*p*, 9*p*, 11*p*, 7*p*, 21*p*}.

4.4
Put the members of the following sets in order of size, smallest first.
(1) {eagle, swallow, robin, blackbird}
(2) {1 *mm*, 1 *km*, 1 *cm*, 1 *m*}
(3) {6, 11, 17, 8, 9, 4, 18}
(4) {giraffe, kangaroo, ostrich}.

4.5
We have seen some examples of the use of larger than, smaller than, etc., but is it always obvious which is the largest or which is the smallest? For example, which is the larger, an elephant or a giraffe? Here we have a problem; the elephant is heavier than the giraffe but the giraffe is taller than the elephant—which then is the larger? If we are interested in weight, then the elephant is. If we are interested in height, then the giraffe is. In some cases, then, we must know just what we are using to judge the size of things, for example, weight, length, height, etc.
In each of the following sets list the members in order of weight, largest first. (You will need to use the school or public library or a good set of encyclopaedias to answer some of them.)
(1) {elephant, rhinoceros, alligator}
(2) {*Queen Mary, United States, Victory*}
(3) {Spitfire, Comet, Boeing 707}
(4) {*Flying Scot, Tal-y-llyn, The Rocket*}.

4.6
The following sets are to be given in order of length or height, smallest first.
(1) {elephant, rhinoceros, alligator}
(2) {*Queen Mary, Queen Elizabeth, United States, La France*}
(3) {St Paul's Cathedral, Coventry Cathedral, Canterbury Cathedral}
(4) {Snowdon, Ben Nevis, Scafell}.

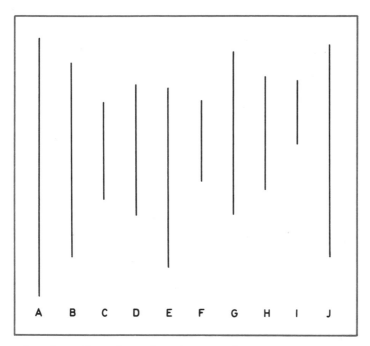

(1) Put the above lines in order, shortest first.
(2) Which lines are longer than line C?
(3) Which lines are longer than line G?
(4) Which lines are shorter than line F?
(5) Which lines are shorter than line B?
(6) Which lines are between C and F, in length, not position?
(7) Which lines are between A and H?
(8) Are any of the lines the same length?

4.8

{7, 11, 15, 12, 10, 8, 3, 25, 31, 64}
(1) Put this set of numbers in order, largest first.
(2) Which numbers are larger than 11?
(3) Which numbers are larger than 25?
(4) Which numbers are smaller than 10?
(5) Which numbers are smaller than 3?
(6) Which numbers are between 8 and 25?
(7) Which numbers are between 11 and 15?
(8) Which numbers are between 25 and 64?

4.9

We have looked at the expressions 'smaller than' and 'larger than' in some detail and in connection with many things. For the remainder of the chapter we are going to deal with the ideas of

'smaller than' and 'larger than' in connection with numbers only.
We know that: 3 is smaller than 4
9 is smaller than 11
7 is larger than 6.
Complete the following statements by putting in the words 'is smaller than' or 'is larger than'.
(1)   3 ––– 7   (2) 7 ––– 3
(3)   2 ––– 6   (4) 6 ––– 2
(5) 18 ––– 19   (6) 9 ––– 8
(7)   6 ––– 1   (8) 0 ––– 10.

4.10

If we have {natural numbers between 0 and 4}, which numbers are members of the set? Is 5 a member? Is 6 a member? Is 4 a member? Is 0 a member?
Your answer to each of these questions should be 'no'. Why is this?
The numbers which are members of the set are {1, 2, 3}.
List the members of the following sets:
(1) {natural numbers between 0 and 3}
(2) {natural numbers between 6 and 12}
(3) {natural numbers less than 7}
(4) {natural numbers less than 5}
(5) {natural numbers greater than 2}
(6) {natural numbers greater than 30}.

4.11

In chapter 2 we used the symbol $\in$ to stand for 'member of' or 'element of'.
4 is a member of {1, 2, 3, 4} was written: $4 \in \{1, 2, 3, 4\}$.
Is the statement $4 \in$ {numbers greater than 0} true?
The set will give us {1, 2, 3, 4, 5, –––}.
We can see that 4 is an element of this set, so that the statement $4 \in$ {numbers greater than 0} is true.
Is the statement $7 \in$ {numbers between 3 and 6} true?
The set will give us {4, 5}. 7 is not an element of this set, so the statement $7 \in$ {numbers between 3 and 6} is not true.
Which of the following statements are true?
(1) $7 \in$ {numbers between 3 and 11}
(2) $6 \in$ {numbers greater than 7}
(3) $2 \in$ {numbers less than 3}
(4) $0 \in$ {numbers less than 2}
(5) $17 \in$ {numbers less than 16}
(6) $11 \in$ {numbers between 11 and 12}.

Consider the sets:

$$A = \{1, 2, 3\} \qquad B = \{0, 1, 2, 3, 4, 5\}.$$

What is the relationship between A and B?

What name do we give to set A?

What symbol do we use for subset?

Which of the following statements are true?

(1) $\{2, 3\} \subset \{$natural numbers$\}$

(2) $\{2, 3\} \subset \{$numbers greater than 2$\}$

(3) $\{2, 3\} \subset \{$numbers less than 4$\}$

(4) $\{2, 3\} \subset \{$numbers between 1 and 4$\}$

(5) $\{5, 6, 7, 8\} \subset \{$numbers between 6 and 12$\}$

(6) $\{5, 6, 7, 8\} \subset \{$numbers larger than 6$\}$.

4.13

In chapter one you found that it was often helpful to draw a diagram to represent a set. The diagram for {natural numbers} might look like this:

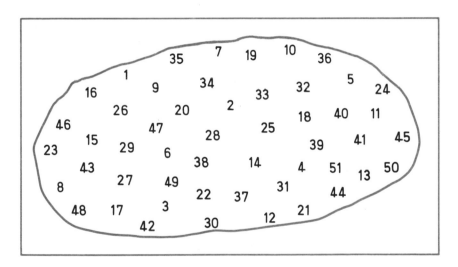

It is rather a jumble of numbers. We cannot put all the numbers in, nor even indicate that there are any more numbers. Mathematicians, who prefer to have things nice and orderly, often take this jumbled up set, stretch it out, and put the numbers in order:

4.13   We can now see the numbers easily and clearly; we still cannot put them all on but we can indicate that there are more numbers than we have shown.

For the natural numbers plus 0 we would have:

We normally use N to stand for {natural numbers}. So, for the natural numbers plus 0 we use N^+, the plus sign showing that we have added 0 to the set N.

Suppose we take {natural numbers greater than 5}. We could put this in a diagram and mark the numbers that we want with a cross:

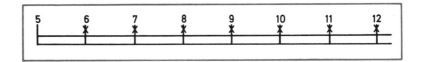

We could put this on the number line for N^+, marking with a cross the numbers that we want:

In a similar way we could represent {numbers between 2 and 5} on a number line:

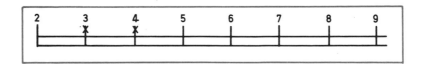

or on the full number line:

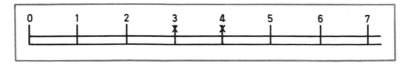

4.14

Draw a full number line for each of the following sets and then mark the sets on the number line as we did in the examples above.
(1) {natural numbers greater than 2}
(2) {natural numbers greater than 1}
(3) {natural numbers less than 6}
(4) {natural numbers less than 5}
(5) {natural numbers less than 1}
(6) {natural numbers between 2 and 4}.

4.15

If we have the two sets:

$$A = \{\text{natural numbers between 3 and 6}\}$$
$$B = \{\text{natural numbers less than 5}\}$$

we could represent them on separate number lines, but what will happen if we put them on the same number line?

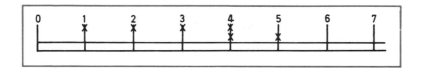

(1) To which set does the number with two crosses belong?
(2) What name do we give to this set?
(3) What symbol do we use for it?

4.16

Mark the following pairs of sets on one number line. What is the intersection of the sets in each case?
(1) {3, 4, 5}   and   {1, 2, 3, 4}
(2) {1, 2, 3}   and   {2, 3, 4, 5}
(3) {natural numbers less than 6}   and
    {natural numbers greater than 4}
(4) {natural numbers greater than 1}   and
    {natural numbers less than 3}
(5) {natural numbers less than 12}   and
    {natural numbers between 8 and 12}
(6) {natural numbers between 6 and 10}   and
    {natural numbers greater than 7}

4.17

In this chapter we have been making considerable use of the expressions 'greater than' and 'less than'. To avoid writing these expressions, mathematicians use shorthand symbols:

> for 'greater than'
< for 'less than'.

Using this shorthand:

5 is greater than 4   becomes $5 > 4$

7 is less than 8   becomes $7 < 8$.

To help you to remember which is which, notice that the point of the symbol points to the smaller number.

4.18
Rewrite the following statements using the shorthand symbol.
(1) 2 is less than 3
(2) 7 is less than 10
(3) 4 is greater than 3
(4) 17 is greater than 7
(5) $6p$ is less than $12p$
(6) 1 g is less than 1 kg.

4.19
By using either $>$ or $<$, complete the following statements:

(1) 5   3   (2) 7   6   (3) 6   7
(4) 11   10   (5) 4   8   (6) 11   12
(7) 17   7   (8) 84   48   (9) 76   77
(10) 23 24   (11) 1   2   (12) 15   5

4.20
Look carefully at the following statements, some are true, some are false. Can you say which are which?

(1) $1 < 3$ (2) $7 > 4$ (3) $6 < 7$
(4) $8 > 9$ (5) $12 < 10$ (6) $15 > 14$
(7) $17 < 21$ (8) $36 > 37$ (9) $41 < 14$
(10) $18 > 8$ (11) $9 < 19$ (12) $72 > 82$.

4.21
Look at the statement: {natural numbers < 5}.
What numbers will fit this statement?
(1) Will 3? i.e., is $3 < 5$?   (2) Will 7? i.e., is $7 < 5$?
(3) Will 4?   (4) Will 5? (Be careful.)
We could write the numbers that fit this statement in the form of a set: {1, 2, 3, 4}.

4.22
Another way of tackling this problem is to draw a number line, mark on it the number 5, and then read off the natural numbers less than 5:

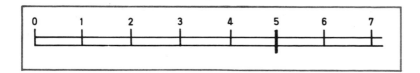

We can now see that the natural numbers less than 5 are {1, 2, 3, 4}, and we can easily see that {6, 7, ---} are all greater than 5.

4.23
What numbers fit the statement: natural numbers > 7?
Can you list them as a set?
Show the set on a number line as we did above.

4.24
Write down the sets of numbers which fit the following statements. Use a number line to help you.
(1) {natural numbers < 6}   (2) {natural numbers > 15}
(3) {natural numbers < 2}   (4) {natural numbers > 1}.

4.25
To make our written work even neater, we can replace the term natural numbers by a letter. Any letter would do, but we shall use the letter x to represent an element of N, thus x ∈ N (read as x is an element of N). Thus:

$$\{natural\ numbers < 5\}\ becomes\ \{x < 5, x \in N\}.$$

The values x could have are 1, 2, 3, 4 or x ∈ {1, 2, 3, 4}.

$$\{natural\ numbers > 3\}\ becomes\ \{x > 3, x \in N\}.$$

The values of x are 4, 5, 6, 7, and so on, or x ∈ {4, 5, 6, 7, ---}.

When we have a set of numbers as our answer or solution, we say that we have found the 'solution set'.
The solution set for x > 10 (x ∈ N) would be {11, 12, 13, 14, ---}.
The solution set for x < 3 (x ∈ N) would be {1, 2}.

4.26
Find the solution set for each of the following statements (x ∈ N). If you need help then use your number line.
(1) x < 7   (2) x > 7
(3) x < 8   (4) x > 15
(5) x < 11   (6) x > 50
(7) x < 2   (8) x > 100
(9) x < 1   (10) 5 < x
(11) 7 > x   (12) 1 < x

4.27
If we have (x + 1) < 5 (where x ∈ N), can you find the solution
set?
What values can x have? Let us try a few and see what happens.
If x = 0 then x is not an element of N.
If x = 1 then x + 1 becomes 1 + 1 = 2 and 2 < 5.
If x = 2 then x + 1 becomes 2 + 1 = 3 and 3 < 5.
If x = 3 then x + 1 becomes 3 + 1 = 4 and 4 < 5.
If x = 4 then x + 1 becomes 4 + 1 = 5 and 5 is not less than 5.
So x = 4 is not a solution. What about x = 6 or x = 7?
The solution set for (x + 1) < 5 is {1, 2, 3}.
Compare this with the solution set for x < 5.
If we represent the solution set for (x + 1) < 5 on a number line
we get:

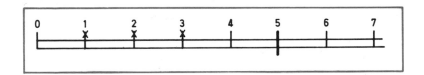

4.28
What is the solution set for the statement x + 2 > 3   (x ∈ N)?
Start by drawing a number line and marking 3 on it:

Now move along the number line checking each number to see if
it fits the statement x + 2 > 3.
We do not need to consider x = 0 since x is not an element of N.
Starting at 1, we have 1 + 2 = 3 and 3 is not greater than 3. At 2,
we have 2 + 2 = 4 and 4 > 3. At 3, we have 3 + 2 = 5 and
5 > 3.
Or we could use the method of 4.27.
If x = 0 then x is not an element of N.
If x = 1 then x + 2 becomes 1 + 2 = 3 and 3 is not greater
than 3.
If x = 2 then x + 2 becomes 2 + 2 = 4 and 4 > 3.
If x = 3 then x + 2 becomes 3 + 2 = 5 and 5 > 3.
So by either method we get the solution set to be {2, 3, 4, 5 ---}.

Use either method to work out the solution sets for the following statements ($x \in N$):

(1) $x + 1 < 3$ (2) $x + 1 > 5$
(3) $x + 2 < 5$ (4) $x + 2 > 5$
(5) $x + 3 < 7$ (6) $x + 3 > 5$
(7) $x + 4 < 5$ (8) $x + 4 > 10$
(9) $x + 5 < 5$ (10) $x + 5 > 5$
(11) $x + 7 > 17$ (12) $x + 2 < 8$.

4.30

Do you remember from chapter two what is meant by 2N, 3N, and 4N?
In a similar way we can write:

$$x + x = 2x$$
$$x + x + x = 3x$$
$$x + x + x + x = 4x$$

Can you suggest a solution set for $2x < 7$?

4.31

If we have the statement $2x < 9$ ($x \in N^+$) what values can x have?
Let us try a few:
if $x = 0$ then $2x = 2 \times 0 = 0$ and $0 < 9$
if $x = 1$ then $2x = 2 \times 1 = 2$ and $2 < 9$
if $x = 2$ then $2x = 2 \times 2 = 4$ and $4 < 9$
if $x = 3$ then $2x = 2 \times 3 = 6$ and $6 < 9$
if $x = 4$ then $2x = 2 \times 4 = 8$ and $8 < 9$
if $x = 5$ then $2x = 2 \times 5 = 10$ and 10 is not less than 9.
What is the value of $2x$ when $x = 6$ and $x = 7$?
Do these values belong to the solution set?
The solution set for $2x < 9$ is $\{0, 1, 2, 3, 4\}$.
If we represent the solution set for $2x < 9$ on a number line we get:

The number line could have been used to find the solution set of $2x < 9$ in a similar way to that of 4.28.

4.32
Find the solution sets for the following (x ∈ N⁺):
(1) 2x < 5   (2) 2x < 7   (3) 2x > 8
(4) 2x > 4   (5) 3x < 9   (6) 3x > 6
(7) 4x < 12   (8) 4x < 4   (9) 5x > 9.

4.33
We have dealt with the symbols for 'greater than' and 'less than', we now need to find some symbols for 'between'. We know that 6 is between 5 and 7. We also know that 5 < 6 and 6 < 7.
Or to save writing 6 twice: 5 < 6 < 7.
This reads: 5 is less than 6 and 6 is less than 7, or 6 is between 5 and 7.
We could also have started the other way round: 7 > 6 and 6 > 5.
Or: 7 > 6 > 5.
This reads 7 is greater than 6 and 6 is greater than 5, or 6 is between 7 and 5.

4.34
Write the following statements using the symbol < :
(1) 7 is between 6 and 8   (2) 11 is between 10 and 13
(3) 17 is between 10 and 20   (4) 12 is between 10 and 20.

4.35
In 4.34 (3) and (4) you had: 10 < 17 < 20 and 10 < 12 < 20.
What other numbers are between 10 and 20?
What is the solution set of numbers between 10 and 20?

4.36
Look at the statement: 5 < x < 10. (x ∈ N⁺.)
What does this tell us? It tells us that x is between 5 and 10.
So x ∈ {6, 7, 8, 9}.
The solution set is {6, 7, 8, 9}.
If we draw a number line to represent the statement 5 < x < 10 we get:

It is easy to see which numbers are between 5 and 10.

Work out the solution sets for the following statements $(x \in N^+)$:

(1) $1 < x < 4$ (2) $2 < x < 8$
(3) $5 < x < 11$ (4) $7 < x < 12$
(5) $12 < x < 13$ (6) $8 > x > 4$
(7) $2 < x + 1 < 6$ (8) $2 < x + 1 < 8$
(9) $4 < x + 2 < 9$ (10) $1 < x + 3 < 7$
(11) $2 < 3x < 10$ (12) $4 < 2x < 10$

(13) Represent your answers to (1), (3), and (7) on number lines.
(14) Represent your answers to (2) and (6) on the same number line.
(15) What is the solution set of the intersection of (2) and (6)?

Interest page

The Metric System

Jim and Mary were very excited. They were going on a continental holiday, touring some European capitals by coach. They had already changed their British currency into continental currencies and had learned the exchange rates for each of the countries they were to visit. In France, the home of the metric system, the pound was worth 11·87 francs, in Belgium 12·20 francs, in Switzerland 10·30 francs, in Germany 9·50 marks, and in Austria 61·20 schillings. (Remember that the decimal point divides the whole units from the part units, thus 11·87 francs is 11 whole francs and 87 centimes, and 10·30 Swiss francs is the same as 10 francs and 30 centimes.) The much awaited day arrived; they flew to Le Touquet where they were met by their British Guide. Jim was very keen to look over the coach, so the driver allowed him to look at the controls and told him about the engine capacity and power. Jim noted that the speedometer went up to 160 k.p.h., i.e., 160 kilometres per hour, and that the petrol tanks held 200 litres of fuel.

The party spent half a day in Brussels. Jim, Mary, and their parents went sight-seeing. Later in the day they went window shopping and at a bookshop bought a book in English about the metric system of weights and measures. That evening Mary and Jim read the book and made the following notes from it:

'In most countries of Europe, the common measure of length is the metre. The metre was originally defined as one ten millionth of the distance along a meridian or line of longitude from the North Pole to the Equator.

$$\text{One metre} = \frac{1}{10,000,000} \text{AB}$$

It was first introduced in France in 1790 soon after the French Revolution.'

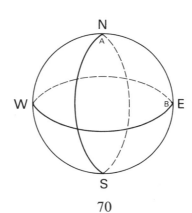

Today, the metre is defined in terms of the wavelength of the orange red line in the krypton gas spectrum (ask your science teacher about this).

The metre is divided into one hundred parts to give centimetres, and multiplied by a thousand to give kilometres. In the metric system, the standard unit of weight is the kilogramme; this is the weight of a standard mass of platinum kept in Paris. One gramme which is one thousandth of a kilogramme is sometimes defined as the weight of one cubic centimetre of water at 4°Celsius.

In scientific work, the gramme is widely used but it is too small for shopkeepers and coalmerchants to use; instead, they use the kilogramme.

The unit of capacity is the cubic centimetre. This is very small.

The practical unit used by the milkman or petrol salesman is the litre. A litre is equivalent to one thousand cubic centimetres.

Now see if you can answer these questions:

(1) If you wished to buy potatoes, would you ask for them in
   (a) kilogrammes   (b) litres   (c) cubic centimetres?
(2) If you wished to buy petrol, would you ask for it in
   (a) grammes   (b) litres   (c) cubic centimetres?
(3) If you wished to buy a carpet, would you ask for it in
   (a) kilogrammes   (b) cubic centimetres   (c) metres?
(4) If you wished to buy coal would you buy it in
   (a) litres   (b) metres   (c) kilogrammes?
(5) Find your own and your neighbour's weight in kilogrammes.
(6) What is your height in (a) metres, (b) centimetres?
(7) Is the length of your pace approximately one metre? Measure it to see.
(8) Is your thumb one centimetre wide? Measure it to find out.
(9) From card, make a box which just holds one litre.
(10) Estimate the weight of this book (a) in kilogrammes, (b) in grammes. Weigh it to check your results.

5. Composition tables

5.1

Look at these two sets of numbers:

$$A = \{1, 2, 3\} \quad \text{and} \quad B = \{4, 5, 6\}.$$

If we wished to add elements from these two sets, we could have:

1 + 4	2 + 4	3 + 4
1 + 5	2 + 5	3 + 5
1 + 6	2 + 6	3 + 6

(1) Look at the first number in each of these additions, what set does it come from?

(2) From which set does the second number come?

(3) Write down the operation that we have used to join elements from each of the sets (A and B) together.

(4) Using the answers to (1), (2), and (3), write down a general statement of all the additions performed above.

All the above additions of elements from sets A and B can be represented in a composition table for A + B:

Set B	6	7	8	9	
	5	6	7	8	
	4	5	6	7	
	+	1	2	3	Set A

5.2

Make out composition tables for addition of the following sets of numbers A and B:

(1) A = {0, 1, 2} B = {3, 4, 5}
(2) A = {0, 1, 2} B = {6, 7, 8}
(3) A = {1, 3, 5} B = {2, 4, 6}
(4) A = {0, 2, 4} B = {2, 4, 6}
(5) A = {0, 2, 4} B = {1, 3, 5, 7, 9}.

Do you notice anything about the numbers inside all these tables (i.e., a pattern that is common to all of them)?

5.3

Look at this table:

Set B	3	3	4	5	6
	2	2	3	4	5
	1	1	2	3	4
	0	0	1	2	3
	+	0	1	2	3	Set A

All of the blue numbers are threes. All of the numbers in the table are found by adding members of set A to members of set B. We can describe all the numbers inside the composition table as A + B, but how can we describe the line of blue numbers? We could say that for this line of squares A + B is equal to 3 and write it in the form of an equation, $A + B = 3$.

Write down the equations which describe the following lines in the composition table:

(1) the line of twos   (2) the line of fours   (3) the line of fives.

5.4

Look at all of the composition tables that we have made so far. In all these tables there are patterns of numbers that lie in straight lines. Is this always the case for composition tables of addition?

5.5

(1) In chapter 2 we discussed the addition of odd and even numbers. Make out a composition table as shown, where O stands for odd numbers and E stands for even numbers.

E		
O		
+	O	E

(2) Make out a composition table for the multiplication of odd and even numbers.

5.6

Look at the set {C, O} where C stands for closed and O stands for open. We can apply this to sight, where one axis of the composition table stands for the right eye and the other for the left eye.

When both eyes are closed we cannot see, so put a C to stand for this. When the left eye is closed and the right eye is open, we can see, so put an O to stand for this.

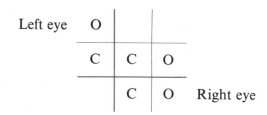

Left eye O		
	C	O
C	C	O
	C	O Right eye

Copy down the table and complete it.

5.7

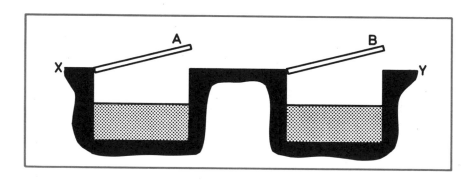

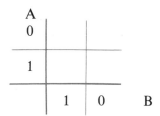

A 0		
1		
	1	0 B

The diagram shows two bridges over adjacent waterways. When a bridge is up it cannot be crossed (put 0 to stand for this). When a bridge is down it can be crossed (put 1 to stand for this). Complete the composition table for this system, putting 1 if it is possible to get from X to Y and 0 if it is not possible.

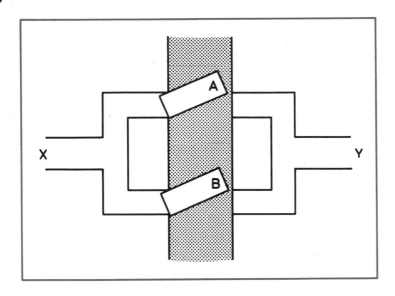

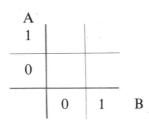

The diagram shows a system of bridges for a canal lock. Complete
the composition table, putting 0 if it is impossible to get from X to
Y and 1 if it is possible.

Look at the tables for 5.5(2), 5.6, 5.7, and 5.8. Can you say anything
about the form of these tables?

In 5.5(2) colour all the E's in the same colour and leave the O's
uncoloured.

In 5.6 colour all the O's in the same colour and leave the C's
uncoloured.

In 5.7 colour all the 0's in the same colour and leave the 1's
uncoloured.

In 5.8 colour all the 1's in the same colour and leave the 0's
uncoloured.

All of these tables have the same form. They are *isomorphic*, 'iso'
meaning 'of the same' and 'morph' meaning 'form'. Can you think
of any other words which include 'iso' or 'morph'?

5.9

(1) Complete the following composition table of addition for the two sets x = {0, 1, 2, 3, 4, 5, 6, 7, 8, 9, 10} and
y = {0, 1, 2, 3, 4, 5, 6, 7, 8, 9, 10} with x horizontal and y vertical.

Set y												
10												20
9												
8									15			
7												
6		7										
5												
4												
3							8					
2												
1		2										
0								7				
+	0	1	2	3	4	5	6	7	8	9	10	Set x

(2) Shade in all the sevens.
(3) Shade in all the tens in a different colour.
(4) Now look at the line of sevens. When x = 7, y = 0. When
x = 6, y = 1.
Write down the values of x and y for the other squares in this line.
For example: when x = 5, y =
                when x = 0, y =
(5) Look at the values of x and y. Can you say anything about
x + y for all of these pairs of values?
(6) Next look at the line of tens. For one of the squares in this line
when x = 6, y = 4, find this square in your composition table.
(7) Copy the following pairs of values of x and y and fill in the gaps.
They all refer to squares in the line of tens:

when x = 1, y = 9   when x = , y = 3

when x = 2, y =   when x = , y = 6

when x = , y = 10   when x = 5, y =

when x = 9, y =   when x = , y = 0

when x = 8, y =   when x — , y = 4

Can x = 13 for this line of squares?

(8) What can you say about x + y for (7)?
Write this down in the form of an equation (i.e., x + y =). The
equation of the line of squares where x + y is 7 is x + y = 7. This
is the general equation for this line of squares in the composition
table for addition of the sets x and y.

(9) Write down the general equations for the lines of squares, in the
composition table for addition, where:

(a) x plus y is equal to 12

(b) x plus y is equal to 9

(c) x plus y is equal to 2.

(10) How many squares are there in each of these lines?
Now look at the answers to 5.9(4).
The equation for this line of squares is x + y = 7.
The set of all values of x and y given in the answer is called the
solution set for x + y = 7 and x and y ∈ N^+ where N^+ stands for
the set of natural numbers plus 0.

Similarly in 5.9(7) the set of values of x and y given for this line of
squares is the solution set for x + y = 10 and x and y ∈ N^+.

(11) Write down the solution sets of values of x and y
(x and y ∈ N^+) for the equations:

(a) x + y = 2   (b) x + y = 9

(c) x + y = 8   (d) x + y = 5.

The number of squares in each line gives the number of solutions in
the solution set. Can you explain this from your composition table?

5.10

If the sets x and y in the composition table for addition were the set
of all natural numbers, how big would the table be?
We do not need to limit our values of x and y to 10; we merely do
this to keep the table small. We do not need an enormous table to
spot the number patterns involved.

5.11

Now make out another composition table of addition for the same sets,
x ∈ {0, 1, 2, 3, 4, 5, 6, 7, 8, 9, 10} and y ∈ {0, 1, 2, 3, 4, 5, 6, 7, 8, 9, 10}.

(1) Shade in the squares in the table where x + y = 5.

(2) Can you say anything about the values of x + y for the squares
below this line?

(3) Can you say anything about the values of x + y for the squares above this line?

(4) Now, using a different colour, shade in the squares in the table where x + y = 10.

(5) Shade in the squares where x + y is greater than 10.

(6) Shade in the squares where x + y is less than 5.

(7) How would you describe the squares in your table that are left unshaded? (i.e., what are the values of x + y for these squares?)

5.12

In chapter 4 you used signs for 'greater than' and 'less than'.
Use these signs to shorten the following:

(1) x plus y is greater than ten

(2) x plus y is less than five

(3) x plus y is greater than sixteen

(4) x plus y is greater than three

(5) x plus y is greater than five and less than ten

(6) x plus y is greater than five and less than eight.

Find which sets of squares in the composition table are referred to by each of the above sentences.

5.13 Look at this composition table of addition:

y											
10	10	11	12	13	14	15	16	17	18	19	20
9	9	10	11	12	13	14	15	16	17	18	19
8	8	9	10	11	12	13	14	15	16	17	18
7	7	8	9	10	11	12	13	14	15	16	17
6	6	7	8	9	10	11	12	13	14	15	16
5	5	6	7	8	9	10	11	12	13	14	15
4	4	5	6	7	8	9	10	11	12	13	14
3	3	4	5	6	7	8	9	10	11	12	13
2	2	3	4	5	6	7	8	9	10	11	12
1	1	2	3	4	5	6	7	8	9	10	11
0	0	1	2	3	4	5	6	7	8	9	10
+	0	1	2	3	4	5	6	7	8	9	10 x

Using the symbols $=$, $>$, and $<$ describe the following sets of squares:

(1) the set of squares shaded ▨

(2) the set of squares shaded ☐

(3) the set of squares shaded ▩

In this table when $y = 4$, if we want $x + y$ to take values less than 12 we look at the line where $y = 4$ (shown by the arrows). We know that if $x + y < 12$ the squares we want are shaded in grey. These squares in the line where $y = 4$ have the values 4, 5, 6, 7, 8, 9, 10, 11. Thus we can say that when $y = 4$ the set of values that $x + y < 12$ can take is {4, 5, 6, 7, 8, 9, 10, 11}. Call this set E.

(4) Write down the sets of values that $x + y < 12$ can take for the following values of y. Call each set by a letter of the alphabet.

(a) $y = 2$ set C   (b) $y = 3$ set D
(c) $y = 5$ set F   (d) $y = 6$ set G
(e) $y = 7$ set H   (f) $y = 8$ set I
(g) $y = 9$ set J   (h) $y = 10$ set K
(i) $y = 0$ set A   (j) $y = 1$ set B

Be careful with (i) because all the possible values are not shown in the table.

(5) Write down the sets of values that $x + y < 12$ can take for the following values of x. Again, call each set by a letter of the alphabet.

(a) $x = 2$ set N   (b) $x = 3$ set O
(c) $x = 4$ set P   (d) $x = 5$ set Q
(e) $x = 6$ set R   (f) $x = 7$ set S
(g) $x = 8$ set T   (h) $x = 9$ set U
(i) $x = 10$ set V   (j) $x = 0$ set L
(k) $x = 1$ set M.

(6) Using set brackets, write down the intersections of the following sets:

(a) $E \cap L$ (b) $E \cap O$ (c) $E \cap Q$
(d) $E \cap S$ (e) $G \cap M$ (f) $G \cap P$
(g) $B \cap S$ (h) $C \cap N$ (i) $O \cap D$.

(7) Write down the set of values, that are in the table, of $x + y$ for $x + y > 12$ when $x = 8$.

If we did not limit our values of x and y to values < 11 (i.e., if x and y could be any natural number) could we list all the elements of this set?

(8) Look at all the squares where $x + y < 12$. Can we list all the elements of this set?

(9) Can you explain why one of the answers to the previous two questions is finite and the other infinite?

(10) Write down the set of values, that are in the table, of $x + y > 12$ when $y = 6$.

5.14

(1) Copy the following pairs of values of x and y and fill in the gaps. They all refer to squares in the line of eights in the previous composition table. An example has been done for you.

$$x = 0 \quad y = 8$$

(a) $x = 1 \quad y =$ (b) $x = 2 \quad y =$

(c) $x = \quad y = 5$ (d) $x = \quad y = 4$

(e) $x = \quad y = 3$ (f) $x = 6 \quad y =$

(g) $x = 7 \quad y =$ (h) $x = \quad y = 0.$

(2) Write down the equation of the line of squares where the sum of x and y is 8.

(3) To what set of numbers do all the above values of x and y belong?

(4) Write down the sets of values of x and y for: (a) $x + y = 3$ and (b) $x + y = 6$, where x and y ∈ N^+.

5.15

We can shorten these pairs of values of x and y even more if we always put the x value first and the y value second.

Thus (2, 4) means that $x = 2$ and $y = 4$. What does (4, 2) mean? Does this refer to the same square in the composition table?

We have here a pair of numbers, but it is not simply a pair of numbers because (2, 4) is not the same as (4, 2). The order of the numbers matters; if 2 comes first it means that $x = 2$, but if 4 comes first it means that $x = 4$. These pairs of numbers are called *ordered pairs*.

5.16

Write down the meaning of each of the following ordered pairs:

(1) (2, 6)   (2) (13, 5)   (3) (3, 5)

(4) (7, 15)   (5) (10, 5)   (6) (50, 3)

(7) (100, 150)   (8) (16, 2)   (9) (7, 17).

5.17

Copy the following table and fill in the values of the ordered pairs in the appropriate squares. Some of them have been done for you.

Graph with grid. Points labeled: (1,5), (7,7), (10,4), (5,2), (7,1). Axes labeled y (vertical, 0–10) and x (horizontal, 0–10).

5.18

Find the set of ordered pairs $\{(0, 5), (1, 4), (2, 3), (3, 2), (4, 1), (5, 0)\}$ in the table. What sort of pattern do they form? Can you describe this pattern in the form of an equation? (Notice the similarity between this line and the lines in the previous composition tables of addition.) We have already seen that for patterns like this the sum of x and y is equal to a number, what is the sum of x and y for this set? Is it the same for every ordered pair in the set? Write down the equation, for example, $x + y = $.

5.19

Find the set of ordered pairs $\{(0, 4), (1, 3), (2, 2), (3, 1), (4, 0)\}$. Describe this set and write the sum of x and y in the form of an equation.

5.20

Write the equations of the following sets of ordered pairs:

(1) $\{(0, 6), (1, 5), (2, 4), (3, 3), (4, 2), (5, 1), (6, 0)\}$
(2) $\{(0, 3), (1, 2), (2, 1), (3, 0)\}$
(3) $\{(0, 10), (1, 9), (2, 8), (3, 7), (4, 6), (5, 5), (6, 4), (7, 3), (8, 2), (9,1),$
    $(10, 0)\}$
(4) $\{(0, 8), (1, 7), (2, 6), (3, 5), (4, 4), (5, 3), (6, 2), (7, 1), (8, 0)\}$
(5) $\{(0, 2), (1, 1), (2, 0)\}$

81

(6) $\{(0, 7), (1, 6), (2, 5), (3, 4), (4, 3), (5, 2), (6, 1), (7, 0)\}$
(7) $\{(0, 4), (1, 3), (2, 2), (3, 1), (4, 0)\}$
(8) $\{(0, 9), (1, 8), (2, 7), (3, 6), (4, 5), (5, 4), (6, 3), (7, 2), (8, 1), (9, 0)\}$
(9) $\{(0, 1), (1, 0)\}$
(10) $\{(0, 5), (1, 4), (2, 3), (3, 2), (4, 1), (5, 0)\}$.

5.21

Look at the following set of ordered pairs:

$$\{(0, 12), (1, 10), (2, 8), (3, 6), (4, 4), (5, 2), (6, 0)\}$$

For this set of ordered pairs if we add the x and y values we do not get a number which stays the same for every ordered pair:
for the first ordered pair (0, 12) $x + y = 12$
for the second ordered pair (1, 10) $x + y = 11$
for the third ordered pair (2, 8) $x + y = 10$.
From this we can see that the equation of the set is not simply the sum of x and y equals some number. We require one equation that will fit all the ordered pairs in the set. Find this set in the table of ordered pairs, does it form a pattern? Look at the set of ordered pairs again, do the numbers in the ordered pairs form a pattern? If there is a pattern in the ordered pairs then there must be an equation to fit them:

for the first ordered pair (0, 12) $x = 0,$ $2x = 0,$ $y = 12$
for the second ordered pair (1, 10) $x = 1,$ $2x = 2,$ $y = 10$
for the third ordered pair (2, 8) $x = 2,$ $2x = 4,$ $y = 8$
for the fourth ordered pair (3, 6) $x = 3,$ $2x = 6,$ $y = 6$
for the fifth ordered pair (4, 4) $x = 4,$ $2x = 8,$ $y = 4$
for the sixth ordered pair (5, 2) $x = 5,$ $2x = 10,$ $y = 2$
for the seventh ordered pair (6, 0) $x = 6,$ $2x = 12,$ $y = 0$.
For all of these ordered pairs $2x + y = 12$, and this is the equation of the set because every member of the set fits this equation.

5.22

Write down the equations of the following sets of ordered pairs and find them in the table:
(1) $\{(0, 8), (1, 6), (2, 4), (3, 2), (4, 0)\}$
(2) $\{(0, 5), (2, 4), (4, 3), (6, 2), (8, 1), (10, 0)\}$
(3) $\{(0, 10), (2, 7), (4, 4), (6, 1)\}$.

5.23

Look at the table of ordered pairs again. What can you say about the ordered pairs in the squares that are outlined in blue? This is the set:

$\{(0, 0), (1, 1), (2, 2), (3, 3), (4, 4), (5, 5), (6, 6), (7, 7), (8, 8), (9, 9), (10, 10)\}$.

(1) Can you find an equation between x and y that will describe
this set?
(2) What is the set of ordered pairs which belong to the set where
$x - y = 0$?
(3) Look at the set of ordered pairs:
$\{(1, 0), (2, 1), (3, 2), (4, 3), (5, 4), (6, 5), (7, 6), (8, 7), (9, 8), (10, 9)\}$.
Can you find an equation to describe this set?
(4) Write down the equations of three more sets of ordered pairs
that run parallel to the two previous sets in the table.

5.24

(1) Write down the set of ordered pairs in the table which belong to
the set $2x - y = 4$ and shade this set on your table.
(2) Where is the set of ordered pairs for which $2x - y < 4$ (in
relation to the line of squares $2x - y = 4$)?
Write down five ordered pairs that belong to this set.
(3) Where is the set of ordered pairs in the table for which
$2x - y > 4$? (Again, in relation to the line of squares $2x - y = 4$.)
Write down five ordered pairs that belong to this set. There are
many more patterns and equations that can be found from this
table of ordered pairs. Find and list as many patterns and equations
as you can.

5.25 Recall

(1) For each of the following problems, write down the solution sets
of ordered pairs (x, y) that obey the given conditions.
(a) The sum of two natural numbers (x and y) is 5. Give the equation.
(b) The sum of two natural numbers (x and y) is 8. Give the equation.
(c) The sum of two even numbers (x and y) is 12.
(d) The sum of two odd numbers (x and y) is 10.
(e) The sum of two prime numbers (x and y) is 8.
(f) Three times one natural number x plus another natural number
y is 12. Give the equation.
(g) Four times an even number plus an odd number is 31.
(2) Write down the solution sets of the following problems in the
form of an ordered pair (x, y) where x is the number of 5 pence
pieces needed and y is the number of 10 pence pieces.
(a) The total value of x and y is $25p$.
(b) The total value of x and y is $50p$.
(c) The total value of x and y is $10p$.
(d) The total value of x and y is $30p$.
(e) The total value of x and y is $45p$.

(3) A man wishes to measure the length of his garden path. In order to save himself the trouble of pacing out the length of the whole path, he asks his son to help him. The man starts from one end of the path and his son from the other. They walk towards each other counting the paces as they go. The man takes x steps and his son y steps to the place where they meet. Write down the solution set of ordered pairs (x, y) for the number of *full* strides taken by the man and his son, if the length of the path is ten metres and the length of the man's stride is one metre and his son's half a metre. Write down the equation for this set.

(4) A box contains a selection of blue and red pencils. Write down the solution set of numbers of blue and red pencils in the form of an ordered pair (b, r) if there are fifteen pencils altogether in the box, where b stands for the number of blue pencils and r stands for the number of red pencils and also b > r.

(5) A fishing rod is to be made from two lengths of rod, one of length x metres and the other of length y metres. Write down the solution set of ordered pairs of values of x and y in the form (x, y) if the rod is three metres long, where x and y are natural numbers.

(6) The following diagram shows the position of black and white during a game of draughts. Black has no kings. White has two kings represented by K.

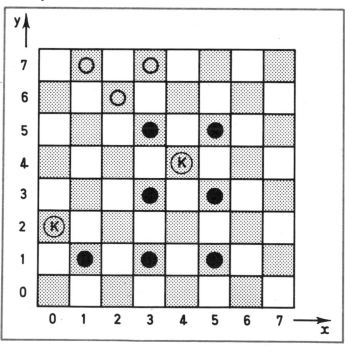

(a) Write down the set of squares in black's possession, in the form of ordered pairs (x, y).

(b) Write down the set of squares in white's possession in the form
of ordered pairs (x, y).
(c) Write down the positions of the two white kings on the board.
(d) If it is white's move, write down one move, which consists of a
series of captures of black men, that will win the game for white.
(e) One diagonal line of white squares consists of $\{(0, 1) (1, 0)\}$ and
has the equation $x + y = 1$. There are six more diagonal lines of
squares which run parallel to this diagonal. List the sets of squares
in each of these diagonals and write the corresponding equations of
each diagonal. Look at the sums of x and y for each white square.
(f) Repeat the above procedure for all of the black diagonals which
run parallel to the white diagonals of (e). Look at the sums of x and
y for each of the black squares.
(g) The sum of the x and y values of a square tells us whether the
square is black or white. Can you explain this?
(7) Although there is no certain way of winning a game of noughts
and crosses, if the second player makes a mistake in his first move,
it is possible for the first player to win. The second player cannot
prevent it. Use the diagram to solve the following problems:

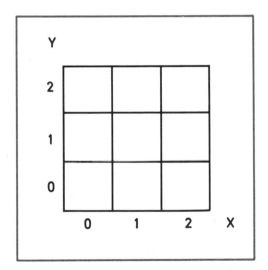

(a) If the first player opens with his nought in square (2, 0), there is
only one possible 'safe' move for the second player. Write this safe
move down in the form of an ordered pair.
(b) If the first player opens with a nought in square (0, 1), there are
four possible safe moves for the second player. Write these down in
the form of a set of ordered pairs.
(c) If the first player opens with a nought in square (1, 1), there are
four possible safe moves for the second player. Write these down in
the form of a set of ordered pairs.

Interest page

Mobiles

Do you know what a mobile is? Perhaps the name mobile is new to you, but you are almost certain to have seen one at some time. You can often see them in grocery shops advertising tea, or in green-grocery shops advertising oranges or bananas. You may also have seen them used as Christmas decorations. Here is a decorative mobile:

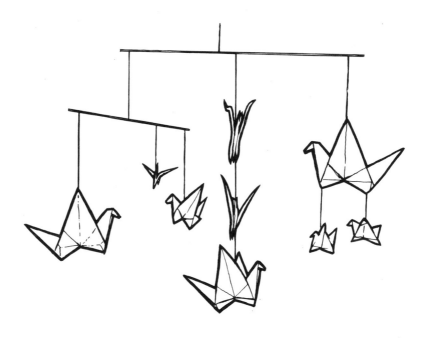

Try making the following fish mobile. Trace the three fishes on page 87 on to coloured card, use a different colour for each size of fish.

Mark on each one the eyes, mouth, etc., and put a faint mark at the balance point. Fix a piece of cotton to the balancing point with a small piece of adhesive tape. Check that the fish 'swims' in the proper position when you hold the cotton.

You can now suspend the fish in any way you like. One example is

shown below. You could either copy this or make up some of your own. Remember that after fixing one fish to another you must check that the fish 'swim' properly. If they do not you must adjust their positions until they do.

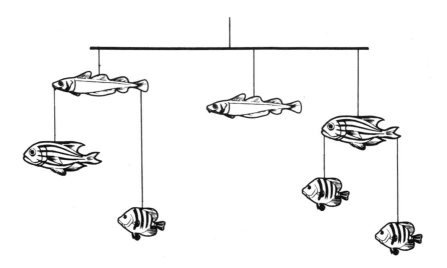

Notice that a crossbar of wood or metal is used in this example. This helps to make a stronger mobile although ideally the crossbar should be part of the mobile.

You can make mobiles by using any shapes you wish; the mathematical shapes of chapter 2, the origami shapes, letters of the alphabet, or any other shapes that may appeal to you.

6. Strange arithmetic

6.1
Let us suppose that an astronaut has landed on Mars and finds living creatures on the planet. The astronaut radios back to Earth a description of the creature. It has two arms, nine short legs, and a head which merges with the body. There are three fingers on each hand.

After some friendly smiles and signs, the astronaut picks up some pebbles in order to find out whether the Martian can count. He arranges them in the pattern below and writes a number under each cluster.

1	2	3	4	5	6	7	8	9	10	11	12	13

The Martian looks at the pattern, then rearranges the pebbles:

1	2	3	4	5	10	11	12	13	14	15	20	21

When we count we use collections of ten. Why is this? The Martian counts in collections of six, why is this?

The astronaut then lays out a row of pebbles and writes a number under each one:

o o o o o o o o o o o o o o o o o o o o o
1 2 3 4 5 6 7 8 9 10 11 12 13 14 15 16 17 18 19 20 21

6.2 The Martian lays out a similar row of pebbles and writes a number under each one:

○ ○ ○ ○ ○ ○　○　○　○　○　○　○　○　○　○　○　○　○　○　○
1 2 3 4 5 10 11 12 13 14 15 20 21 22 23 24 25 30 31 32 33

Using the words (1) one, (2) two, (3) three, (4) four, (5) five, (10) one nought, (11) one one, (12) one two, (13) one three, and so on, to stand for the numbers shown, practise counting in this Martian way. Write down six numbers as we would write them, then change books with your neighbour and change your neighbour's numbers to the Martian way of writing them. See who can get the most right.

6.2

(1) What is your age in Martian numbers?
(2) How many pupils are there in your class according to the Martian way of counting?
(3) The astronaut shows the Martian his two hands, he shows him ten fingers; how would the Martian write ten?
(4) Write today's date in the way the Martian would write it.
(5) Write the number of people in your family in the way the Martian would write it.

6.3

When we count pebbles we normally collect the pebbles into clusters of ten, or we can say that we count in 'base ten' (this is the term used by mathematicians) but the Martian when he counts uses base six (or clusters of six).

Take a bundle of twenty-three straws and lay them out on your desk first as we would count them in clusters of ten. Draw this arrangement.

Now arrange them as the Martian would (i.e., in clusters of six). Draw this arrangement.

There are three clusters of six and five left over, so in Martian counting there would be 35 (three five) straws.

Now take the following bundles of straws and draw diagrams to show how the Martian would arrange them.

(1) 15 straws	(2) 27 straws	(3) 26 straws
(4) 31 straws	(5) 30 straws	(6) 18 straws
(7) 24 straws	(8) 29 straws	(9) 36 straws.

Now write down the figures the Martian would use to describe the number of straws in each question.

6.4

The following numbers are in base ten (our language). Change them to base six (Martian language).

A diagram of straws might help you.
(1) 7   (2) 5   (3) 9
(4) 16   (5) 25   (6) 34
(7) 33   (8) 19   (9) 40.

6.5
Now try changing these numbers from base six (Martian language)
to base ten (our language). A diagram of straws might help you.
(1) 3   (2) 5   (3) 14
(4) 23   (5) 34   (6) 54
(7) 43   (8) 4   (9) 45.

6.6
The astronaut shows the Martian forty-five pebbles:

45 pebbles

He asks the Martian to rearrange the pebbles and count them for
him. The Martian rearranges the pebbles:

113 pebbles

Notice that there is one collection of thirty-six, one of six, and three
left over. So the Martian writes 113 (one one three) pebbles.
How many clusters of thirty-six can be taken out of the following?
(1) eighty pebbles   (2) one hundred and sixteen pebbles
(3) ninety pebbles   (4) ninety-nine pebbles.
(5) Working with your neighbour and sharing your straws, make
up the patterns that the Martian would use to count each of the
above collections of pebbles. Put your answers in columns. The
first one is done for you.

91

Number in base ten (our language)	Number in base six (Martian language)		
	36's	6's	1's
80	2	1	2
116			
90			
99			

6.7

Copy this table and fill in the blanks:

	Number in base ten (our language)	Number in base six (Martian language)		
		36's	6's	1's
(1)	60	1		0
(2)	71		5	5
(3)	75	2		
(4)	83			
(5)	120		2	
(6)		1	2	2
(7)		2	1	3
(8)	41			
(9)		1	0	1
(10)	26			
(11)	153			
(12)		2	3	4

(1) A boy has two boxes, one will hold 36 marbles, the other 6 marbles. His father gives him 57 marbles.

(a) How many times can he completely fill the large box from the 57 marbles?

(b) With the marbles left over, how many times can he completely fill the smaller box?

(c) How many marbles are now left over?

(d) What is 57 (base ten) in base six?

(2) Supposing the boy had been given 125 marbles.

(a) How many times would he be able to completely fill the large box?

(b) With the marbles left over how many times could he fill the smaller box?

(c) How many would be left over?

(d) What is 125 (base ten) in base six?

(3) Answer the same questions if the boy had been given: (a) 93, (b) 37, (c) 72, (d) 117 marbles.

(4) A man has a twenty-five litre, a five litre, and a one litre container. A tank contains ninety-seven litres of liquid.

(a) How many times can the twenty-five litre container be completely filled from the tank?

(b) How many times can the five litre container be filled from the liquid that is left in the tank?

(c) From the liquid that is left, how many times can the one litre container be filled? Assume that no liquid is spilled.

(d) What is ninety-seven (base ten) in base five?

(5) Answer the same question for a tank containing 117 litres.

(6) Can the number 126 exist in base six?

(7) Write down the next three terms of these series and state which base they are in.

(a) 1, 3, 10, 12, 14, ---

(b) 3, 10, 13, 20, ---

(c) 5, 11, 16, ---.

6.9

Let us return to the Martian and the astronaut. The Martian takes the astronaut to a school where he sees children doing arithmetic. He looks over the shoulder of one boy and sees the following written on his page:

(1) $\begin{array}{r} 3 \\ +4 \\ \hline 11 \end{array}$ ✓	(2) $\begin{array}{r} 4 \\ +5 \\ \hline 13 \end{array}$ ✓	(3) $\begin{array}{r} 5 \\ -4 \\ \hline 1 \end{array}$ ✓

(4)
```
   12
 +  5
 ───
   21  √
```

(5)
```
   12
 −  5
 ───
    3  √
```

(10)
```
    2
  × 3
  ───
   10  √
```

(11)
```
    4
  × 3
  ───
   20  √
```

(12)
```
 3)13
   3  √
 ───
```

The boy is waiting to have some others marked, they are:

(13)
```
    4
  + 4
  ───
   12
```

(14)
```
    1
  + 5
  ───
   10
```

(15)
```
   11
 + 14
 ────
   25
```

(20)
```
   13
 + 24
 ────
   41
```

(21)
```
   13
 −  5
 ────
    4
```

(22)
```
   24
 −  5
 ────
   14
```

Are these questions right or wrong?

6.10
Now try some for yourself.

(1)
```
    2
  + 5
  ───
```

(2)
```
    3
  + 5
  ───
```

(3)
```
   15
 +  4
 ───
```

(4)
```
   12
 + 14
 ───
```

(5)
```
   42
 + 35
 ───
```

(6)
```
   51
 + 43
 ───
```

(7)
```
   25
 − 12
 ───
```

(8)
```
   41
 − 32
 ───
```

(9)
```
   42
 − 14
 ───
```

(10)
```
   50
 − 24
 ───
```

(11)
```
   33
 − 24
 ───
```

(12)
```
   45
 − 10
 ───
```

(13)
```
   123
 + 145
 ─────
```

(14)
```
   415
 + 232
 ─────
```

(15)
```
   412
 − 334
 ─────
```

(16)
```
   545
 − 345
 ─────
```

(17)
```
   24
 ×  3
 ───
```

(18)
```
   34
 ×  2
 ───
```

94

6.11

One girl in the class is working with an abacus.
She is adding the numbers 4 and 3 and 14 (base six) on the abacus.
She moves four beads in the units row to the right-hand side, counting as she does it:

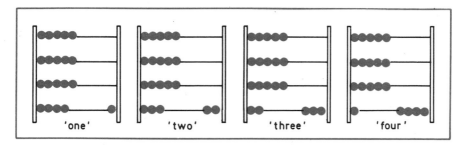

Next she adds on the three, again counting as she does it:

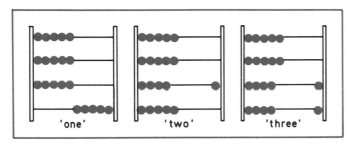

Now she adds on the one four:

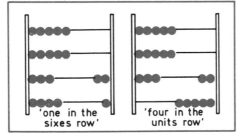

(1) What is the answer in base six to 4 + 3 + 14?
(2) What would this answer be if changed to base ten?
(3) What is the largest number that can be represented on this abacus in base six?
(4) Change the answer you obtained in (3) to base ten.

6.12
The abacus was invented many years ago. There are three main types in existence today. Find out who invented the abacus and the names of the three types. (See, for example, *Calculating Devices*, Exploring Mathematics Series, ed. J. Palframan and published by McGraw-Hill.)
Working in pairs, make a simple abacus for counting in base ten. Cut out from card twenty-seven two-centimetre squares. On a sheet of A3 or A4 paper draw three pairs of straight lines two centimetres apart. Now place the squares as shown in the diagram:

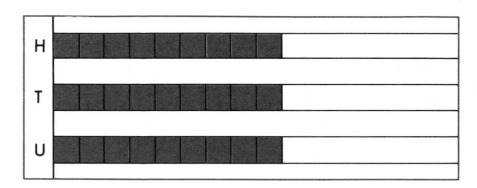

Name the rows H, T, and U as above. If the abacus represented seven, it would look like this:

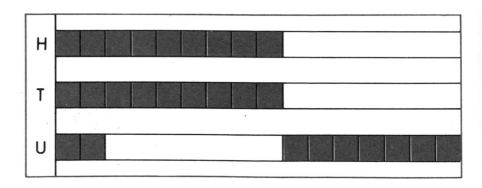

6.13
Represent the following numbers on your abacus:

(1) 8	(2) 12	(3) 15	(4) 19	(5) 9
(6) 0	(7) 21	(8) 30	(9) 73	(10) 136.

How would you use your abacus to add 6 and 7? Discuss this with your neighbour. The programme for performing this addition would be:

(1) Move six squares to the right-hand side of row U.

(2) Move three more squares to the right-hand side of row U. There are now none left in row U.

(3) Move one square across in row T and return all squares in row U.

(4) Move three squares across in row U. The abacus should now look like this:

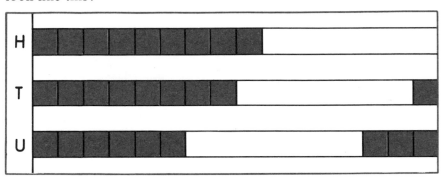

This way of working is slow on a card abacus since the cards are difficult to move, but with the abacus shown in 6.11 the working would be much quicker as the counters move easily.

6.15

On the card abacus row U is the units row, row T the tens row, and row H the hundreds row. What is the largest number that can be represented on this card abacus?

6.16

Use your abacus to work out the following:

(1) 6 + 8   (2) 7 + 9   (3) 8 + 10

(4) 11 + 7   (5) 15 + 12   (6) 141 + 316.

6.17

So far in this chapter we have worked mainly in base six. For base ten the digits forming a number are worth:

100 or 10 × 10	10 10	1 1
4	2	3

6.18 This number is four hundred and twenty-three.
For base six the columns are worth:

	36 6 × 6	6 6	1 1
	2	3	4

This number is two three four (base six).
The columns for base five are worth:

	25 5 × 5	5 5	1 1
	3	2	4

This number is three two four (base five).
What are the first three columns worth for:
(1) base three   (2) base seven
(3) base nine   (4) base two?
(5) How many beads would be required on each wire of an abacus if it was used to represent numbers in (a) base three, (b) base five.

6.18
(1) Change your age into (a) base five, (b) base three.
(2) Change today's date into base seven.
(3) Change the number of pupils in your form into base four.
(4) Change the number of this page into base seven.
(5) These 'sums' are worked in base four. Complete the table:

$$1 + 0 = 1 \qquad\qquad 2 + 1 =$$
$$1 + 1 = 2 \qquad\qquad 2 + 2 = 10$$
$$1 + 2 = \qquad\qquad 2 + 3 = 11$$
$$1 + 3 = \qquad\qquad 3 + 1 =$$

(6) Copy this composition table and complete it. The answers will help you.

3				
2	2		10	
1		2		
0				3
+	0	1	2	3

(7) Copy this composition table and complete it. First find the base in which it is worked.

+	0	1	2	3	4	5
5				12		
4					12	
3				10		
2						
1		2				
0						

(8) Have the tables in (6) and (7) any special property?
(9) Does $5 + 4 = 4 + 5$ in base six?
(10) In base four does $3 + 2 = 2 + 3$?
(11) In base six does $1 + 2 = 2 + 1$?
(12) Would $a + b = b + a$ if a and b are numbers in base six?
This property of numbers is called the *commutative law for addition*.

6.19
State the base in which each of these is worked.

(1)   5
     +4
     ‾12‾

(2)   5
     +4
     ‾13‾

(3)   5
     +4
     ‾11‾

(4)   5
     +4
     ‾10‾

(5)   15
     +16
     ‾33‾

(6)   121
     − 14
     ‾102‾

(7)   121
     − 14
     ‾105‾

(8)   22
     × 2
     ‾110‾

(9)   14
     × 2
     ‾32‾

6.20
Work the following in the bases stated:

(1)   13
     +24
     ‾‾‾‾ base 6

(2)   32
     +16
     ‾‾‾‾ base 8

(3)   34
     +12
     ‾‾‾‾ base 5

6.21

(4)	$\begin{array}{r} 21 \\ -12 \\ \hline \end{array}$ base 3	(5)	$\begin{array}{r} 16 \\ \times\ 3 \\ \hline \end{array}$ base 7	(6)	2)12 base 4

(7) $\begin{array}{r} 217 \\ -143 \\ \hline \end{array}$ base 8　(8) $\begin{array}{r} 1010 \\ +\ 111 \\ \hline \end{array}$ base 2　(9) $\begin{array}{r} 416 \\ -214 \\ \hline \end{array}$ base 7

(10) $\begin{array}{r} 222 \\ -\ 33 \\ \hline \end{array}$ base 5　(11) $\begin{array}{r} 312 \\ \times\ 12 \\ \hline \end{array}$ base 4　(12) $\begin{array}{r} 283 \\ \times\ 27 \\ \hline \end{array}$ base 9

(13) Which digits are used in arithmetic: (a) base six, (b) base eight, (c) base two, (d) base five?

(14) These digits are used in arithmetic to a certain base 0, 1, 2, 3, 4, 5, 6. What is the base?

(15) Change the date 1066 to base seven.

(16) Change the date 1939 to base eight.

(17) Copy this table and fill in the blanks so that the numbers on each row are equivalent.

Base ten	Base six	Base four	Base two	Base seven
5				
		13		
	214			
			1010	
				63

6.21

Find out about the Imperial system of weights and measures then fill in the blanks in the following tables:

Weight

—— ozs make 1 lb (base ——)
—— lbs make 1 stone (base ——)
2 stones make —— qtrs (base ——)
4 —— make 1 —— (base ——)
—— cwts make 1 ton (base ——)

Length

      12 ——   make 1 ft (base ——)
       3 ——   make 1 —— (base ——)
    220 ——   make 1 —— (base ——)
  —— furlongs make 1 —— (base ——)

Capacity

    2 pints make —— —— (base ——)
    4 —— make —— —— (base ——)

6.22

The Metric System of weights and measures has a base of ten. Find out about the Metric System, then complete the tables below. The abbreviations normally used are given in brackets after each unit.

Weight

    1000 grammes (*g*) make 1 ——
  —— kilogrammes (*kg*) make 1 metric ton (tonne)

Length

    10 millimetres (*mm*) make ——
    100 centimetres (*cm*) make —— metre (*m*)
    1000 millimetres (*mm*) make —— metre (*m*)
  —— metres (*m*) make 1 kilometre (*km*)

Capacity

    1000 cubic centimetres (*cm*³) make ——
  —— litres (*l*) make 1 cubic metre (*m*³)

Money

    100 new pence (*p*) make ——

Time

The measure for time is not to base 10 but to base 60. Find out why.

    60 seconds (*s*) make 1 minute (*min*)
    60 —— make —— hour (*h*)

6.23

Now try these questions:

(1) Estimate the weight of your friends in kilogrammes.

(2) What is the length of (a) your foot in centimetres, (b) your stride in metres?

(3) What is your waist measurement in centimetres?

(4) Estimate the length and breadth of your classroom in metres. Check by measurement.

(5) Find out the length of a football pitch or hockey pitch in metres. Work the following:

(6) £0·69 + £3·47   (7) 2·96 *m* + 4 *mm*

(8) 2·6 litres + 250 cm^3 (9) 2 hours 14 minutes +
3 hours 57 minutes

(10) Change 1579 metres to kilometres

(11) Change £4·90 to pence

(12) Change 2·73 metres to centimetres

(13) Change 3 cubic metres to litres.

(14) A grocer drops 3 trays of eggs, each of which contains 30 eggs. If the eggs cost him 1*p* each, how much money has the grocer lost if all the eggs are smashed?

(15) Mary went shopping. She spent 10 minutes at the butcher's, twice as long at the Post Office, and 15 minutes at the grocer's. How long did she spend in the three shops?

(16) John spends 35 minutes on his French homework, 27 minutes on his mathematics homework, and 45 minutes on his Latin. How long does his homework take?

(17) On one Saturday morning David agrees to clean the family car for 25*p*. It takes him 75 minutes. He then goes shopping which takes him 35 minutes and earns him 15*p*. Finally he agrees to cut the lawn for 25*p*. This takes him 40 minutes.

(a) How much does he earn?

(b) How long does he take to earn his pocket money?

(c) How much is this per hour?

6.24 Recall

(1) If   16   what is   43   ?
$$+23 \qquad -26$$
$$\overline{42} \qquad \overline{}$$

(2) What is 31 (base six) in base ten?

(3) What is 46 (base ten) in base three?

(4) Work the following in the bases stated:

(a)   124
$$+213$$
_____ base 5

(b)   132
$$-\ 24$$
_____ base 6

(c) 3)413
___ base 5

(d)   214
$$\times\ \ 6$$
_____ base 7

(5) Which of the following are true:

(a)   413
$$+\ 26$$
$$\overline{442}\ \text{base 7}$$

(b)   263
$$\times\ \ 4$$
$$\overline{1183}\ \text{base 9}$$

(6) Change:
(a) 5·7 kilogrammes to grammes
(b) 2 kilometres to metres
(c) 1200 metres to kilometres.

(7) What is
(a) 3·7 litres in cubic centimetres
(b) 14,000 cubic centimetres in litres
(c) 2 hours 14 minutes in minutes
(d) 215 minutes in hours and minutes?

(8) In a competition three people share equally a prize of £3·36. How much does each receive?

(9) Mr Smith invests £100 in a business, Mr Jones invests twice as much, and Mr Brown invests five times as much as Mr Smith How much money do the three men invest between them?

(10) A journey of 100 kilometres by coach costs £1. How much would a journey of 45 kilometres cost?

(11) At a jumble sale 60 people paid the entrance fee of 3p and each of them spent at least 5p. What is the smallest sum of money the organizers can collect?

(12) Each day at school 640 pupils drink a carton of milk, each carton contains 150 cm^3. How much milk to the nearest litre is drunk each day?

(13) On the first night of the school play, 134 adults paid 10p for their seats and 100 children paid 5p for their seats. How much money was taken at the box office?

(14) Codes
Jack sent the following coded message to his friend Ron:

$$100, 30, 41, 1, 33, 10, 1, 31, 1, 22.$$

Ron knows that Jack likes working in base five. So he writes out the alphabet and starting at A, numbers the letters in base five:

A	B	C	D	E	F	---
1	2	3	4	10	11	---

Complete this table and decode the message.
Send a message to your neighbour using this code.
Make up some codes of your own.

Interest page

History of Measuring

In chapter 4 we were looking at the size of things. When we want to
find out the size of something we generally measure it or weigh it.
We know that two people measuring the same thing should get
the same result. This has not always been the case; let us look back
in history and see how measuring was carried out before the
introduction of standardized rulers and tape measures. A man
wishing to measure the length of a piece of wood might lay it on the
ground and measure the length of it by using his feet. He would
first place the heel of one foot level with the end of the wood.
He would then place the heel of his other foot so that it just touched
the toe of his first foot. As he walked along the side of the piece
of wood, heel to toe, he would count the number of foot lengths.
If his friend then measured the wood, using the same method,
would he get the same answer?
Measure the length and width of your classroom using the heel to
toe method.
Will everyone get the same result?
Using a ruler, measure the length of your foot and the length of the
feet of various adults. Are any of these measurements anywhere
near the same?
Suppose the man now wishes to measure the width of his piece of
wood. The heel to toe method would probably be unsuitable as his
foot is likely to be too big, so what can he use? A very convenient
part of the body for small measurements of this sort is the thumb.
The man could easily measure the wood using his thumbs
alternately.
How many thumb widths is this page?
What is the length of this page in thumb widths? Will everyone get
the same result?
What is the length and width of your desk in thumb widths?
Mark the length of your foot on a piece of paper, how many
thumb widths long is your foot?
Check the width of your thumb against a ruler.
Check the width of the thumbs of various adults.

If we go into a shop today to buy a length of material we ask for so many yards; the material is laid out on the counter and measured with a tape measure or measuring machine.

Before the invention of tape measures and rulers, how could a man measure a length of material? He would obviously not want to lay it out on the ground and then walk on it to find the number of foot lengths. The method he used was to take one end of the material in one hand and then stretch his arm out sideways; with his other hand he would pull the cloth tight until his fingers just touched his nose when he was facing forward.

This was one length. He would then let the outer end go and take hold of the cloth near his nose and again stretch his arm out straight. He then had two lengths, and so on.

If his friend used the same method for measuring the same cloth, would he get the same result?

By using a piece of string or tape, find the distance from the tip of your nose to the tip of your outstretched finger. Lay the string or tape on the floor and see how many foot lengths this equals.

Check the nose to fingertip measurement of various adults.

In the above work you should have found (as our ancestors did) that the following table is approximately true:

> 12 thumbs = 1 foot
> 3 feet   = 1 outstretched arm.

As time passed it was decided that this system of measuring (using thumbs or feet, etc.) was not accurate enough and that everyone should be able to get the same results when measuring the same things. So a piece of metal was cast. Its length was the nose to finger distance of one man; this length was called a yard. The yard was divided into three equal parts. Each part was called a foot. Each foot was divided into twelve and called an inch. Other pieces of wood and metal were then marked off using this standard yard as a guide, thus giving us the rulers and tape measures which we have today. The original piece of metal, the standard yard, is still in use and is kept at the National Physical Laboratory in London.

Further research
Find out all you can about the origin of the following units of measurement:

(1) hands	(2) furlong	(3) pole
(4) rod	(5) perch	(6) metre.

7. Balancing

7.1

Do you know the name of the man who walked on a tightrope over Niagara Falls, one of the largest waterfalls in the world? Find out all you can about this man and his daring acts, which included pushing a wheelbarrow with a man in it across Niagara Falls. He was the world's best tightrope walker and as such needed a perfect sense of balance.

All of the pictures at the beginning of this chapter are to do with balance and balancing. You probably found when you made your mobiles that great care was needed to get them to balance. The second picture shows a see-saw; have you ever tried balancing a see-saw so that it is horizontal and not moving? It is quite difficult. The remaining pictures are of two instruments or balances that are used for weighing everyday items.

The art of balancing depends on having the same or equivalent things on opposite sides of a central point. Where must the pivot be for the following scales to balance?

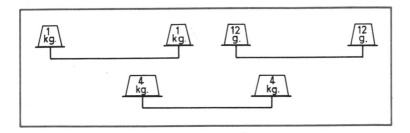

(1) Take two 25 *cm* rules, hold one on its edge and try to balance the other across it.

(2)

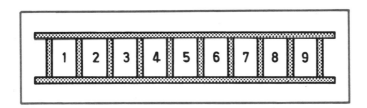

If you had to pick up this ladder, at which point would you take hold of it?

Why would space 1 and space 9 be rather silly places to choose?

(3) Why does a tightrope walker often use a pole?

7.2

If we have a see-saw like this:

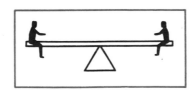

and we know that the see-saw is balanced, what can we say about the two people on the see-saw?

7.3 The see-saws in the following two pictures are also balanced:

What can you say about the people balancing the see-saws?

7.3
What can you say about the boxes on each of the following scales?
In each case the scales are balanced.

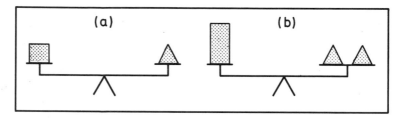

7.4
If we give names to the boxes we have been using we can write down simple statements about the balance.
We will let the weight of the square box be S
              the weight of the triangular box be T
              the weight of the rectangular box be R.
Look at the balance below:

From it we see that:
the square box is equivalent to the triangular box
or   weight of square box = weight of triangular box
or   S = T.
The same applies to:

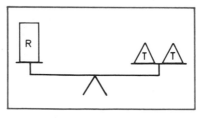

108

From it we see that:

    the rectangular box is equivalent to two triangular boxes
or weight of rectangular box = weight of two triangular boxes
or R = 2T.
If we have:

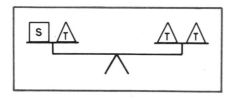

From it we see that:

    a square box and a triangular box are equivalent to two tri-
    angular boxes
or weight of square box plus weight of triangular box = weight of
    two triangular boxes
or S + T = 2T.
The statement we have made about each balance:

$$S = T \qquad R = 2T \qquad S + T = 2T$$

is called the equation of the balance.

7.5
For each of the following balances, write down the equation of the
balance:

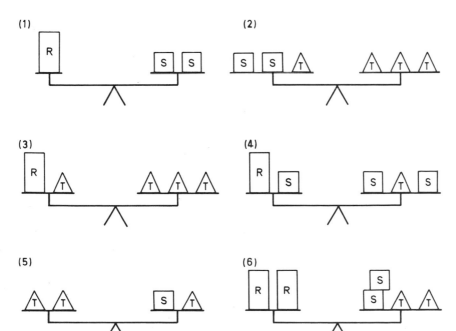

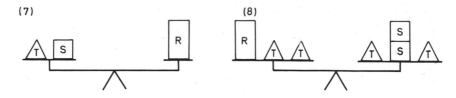

7.6

The balances shown below are incomplete; complete them by putting in the appropriate box or boxes and then write down the equation of the balance. (There are several possible answers in some cases.)

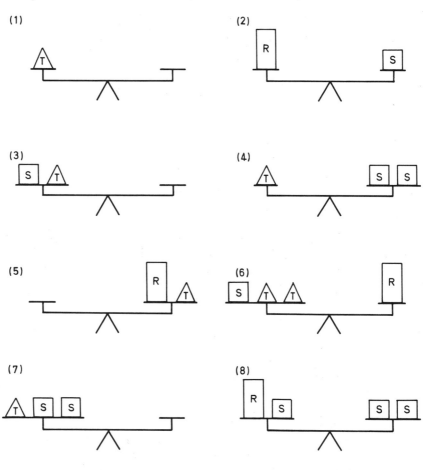

7.7

Draw balances to represent the following equations:
(1) $2T = S + T$ (2) $R = 2S$
(3) $3T = R + S$ (4) $R + T = 3S$
(5) $2R + T = 3S + 2T$ (6) $2S + 2T = 2R.$

Now look at some balances with actual weights on them:

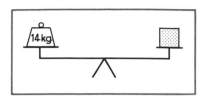

What must the weight of the box be?
The weight of the box must be 14 *kg* to balance the scales. That was
fairly simple; what about the next one?

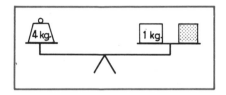

What is the weight of the box in this case?
Still fairly easy; what happens in the next one?

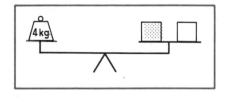

What are the weights of the boxes?
A little more care is needed here as there are several possible
answers. If we allow only units of 1 *kg* (i.e., 1 *kg*, 2 *kg*, 3 *kg*, 4 *kg*,
etc.) there are three possible answers; what are they?

7.9
In 7.8 you should have for your answers:

7.10 We have a set of answers and therefore could write down our answer in set form, with the blue box values first:

$$\{(1 \ kg, 3 \ kg), (2 \ kg, 2 \ kg), (3 \ kg, 1 \ kg)\}.$$

What set of weights could we use to balance the following?

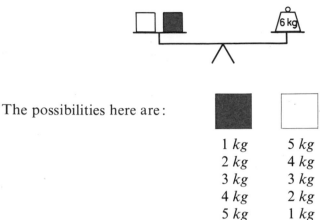

The possibilities here are:

🟫	⬜
1 kg	5 kg
2 kg	4 kg
3 kg	3 kg
4 kg	2 kg
5 kg	1 kg

So the set of solutions, blue box values first, would be:

$$\{(1 \ kg. 5 \ kg), (2 \ kg, 4 \ kg), (3 \ kg, 3 \ kg), (4 \ kg, 2 \ kg), (5 \ kg, 1 \ kg)\}.$$

7.10

For each of the following balances write down the set of possible weights that will balance it:

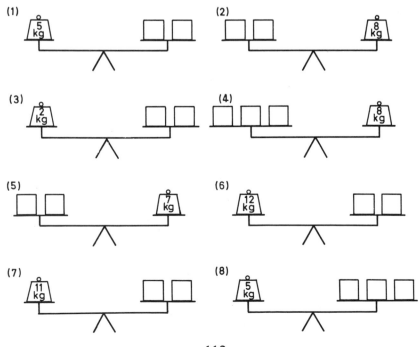

By using your answers to 7.8, 7.9, and 7.10, complete the following table:

Wt	Number of possible ways of balancing it using two weights
2 kg	1
3 kg	
4 kg	
5 kg	
6 kg	5
7 kg	
8 kg	
9 kg	

Can you see a pattern in your results?
How many ways could you balance (a) a 20 kg weight (b) a 47 kg weight (c) an n kg weight?

7.12
Will this system balance?

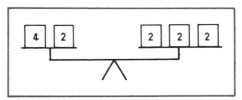

Be careful with your answer. The system will only balance if the weights referred to are in the same units.
This obviously would not balance.

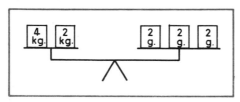

But these would:

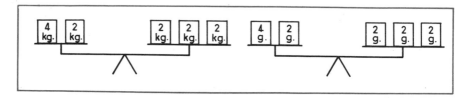

As long as we know that the units are all the same, then the system will balance.

In the rest of the chapter and, in fact, in the rest of your work, whenever a balance or balance equation is used you can be sure that all parts are in the same units, unless otherwise stated. So it would be quite true to say that the following will balance:

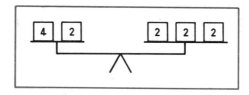

7.13

Using the above balance what will happen if we take the $\boxed{2}$ from the left-hand side?
What can you do to restore the balance? (There are two possible answers.)

7.14

The two possibilities for 7.13 are:
(1) Put it back.

(2) Take a $\boxed{2}$ from the right-hand side.

In the following, what happens if the $\boxed{3}$ is removed from the right-hand side?

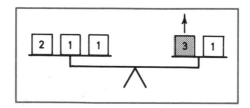

What must be done to the left-hand side to restore the balance?
In each of the following, what happens if the blue weight is

removed? What must be done to the other side to restore the
balance?

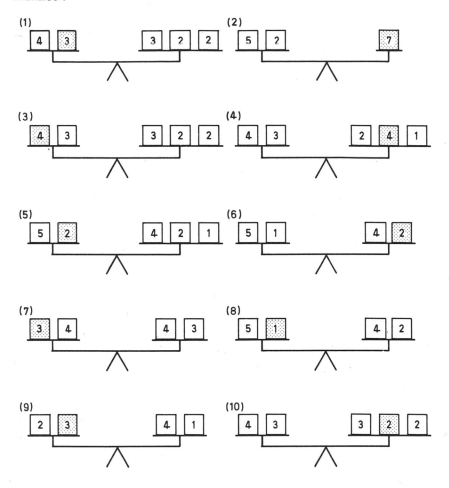

7.15
What would happen to the balance below if we added a weight to
one side?

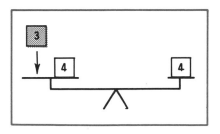

What must be done to restore balance? (There are two possibilities.)
In each of the following, what happens if the blue weight is added

to the balance? What must be done to the other side to restore the balance?

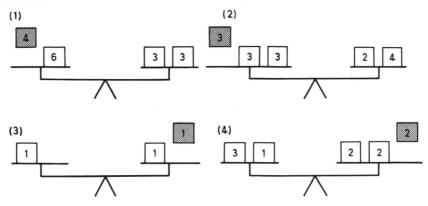

7.16

We have seen in 7.14 and 7.15 the *golden rule of the balance* in operation.

If you add something to one side you must add the same thing to the other side.

If you take something from one side you must take the same thing from the other side.

In other words, whatever you do to one side, you must do to the other, if balance is to be maintained. This rule applies to all equations.

7.17

Earlier in this chapter we used an empty box when we were not sure of the value that it should have:

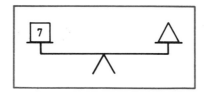

What value goes in the empty box?

To make our work more mathematical and easier to write down we could use a letter to represent the value in the box:

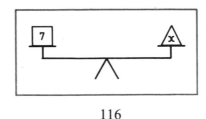

The value of the box must be 7.

So we write x = 7.

Any letter would do, but as your mathematical knowledge increases, you will find that various letters of the alphabet are used to represent particular things. To avoid confusion later on we will start now by using the letter most used by mathematicians for this sort of work, i.e., the letter x.

7.18

In the earlier part of the chapter you were writing down the equations of balances. In 7.17 you were doing the same thing. Now look at the following:

Example 1

The equation for the balance:

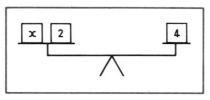

would be │ x │ and │ 2 │ is equivalent to │ 4 │ or x + 2 = 4.

We can see from the balance that the value represented by x is 2, i.e., x = 2.

(*Note:* we might also have found the value of x by taking 2 from both sides.)

Example 2

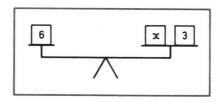

The equation of the balance is: 6 = x + 3.

From the balance we see that: x = 3.

(*Note:* we might also have found the value of x by taking 3 from both sides.)

In each of the following cases write down the equation of the balance and, where you can, say what value x stands for:

(1)   (2)

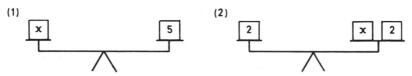

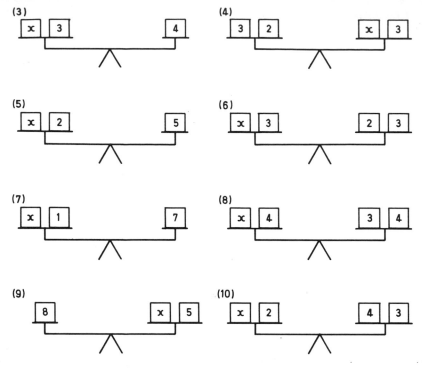

What would be the equation of the following balance?

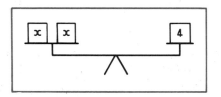

We have 2 boxes of x = 4

$$x + x = 4$$

or $\qquad 2x = 4$

What is the value of x?

The following balance gives:

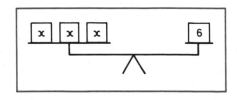

$$x + x + x = 6$$

or $\qquad\qquad 3x = 6$

What is the value of x?

Look carefully at the next one:

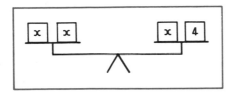

The equation for this balance would be:
$$x + x = x + 4$$
or $$2x = x + 4$$
What is the value of x?
Write down the equation for this balance:

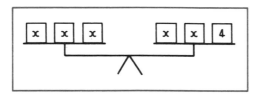

What is the value of x?

7.20
In each of the following cases write down the equation of the balance and, where you can, find the value of x.

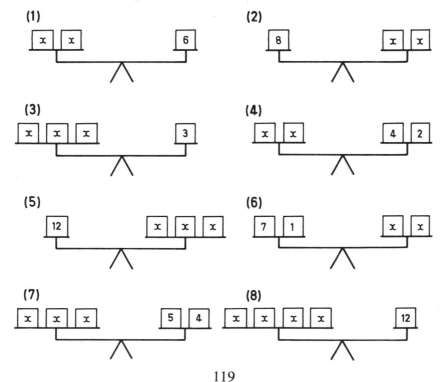

(9)   **(10)**

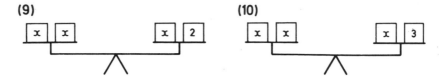

7.21
Which of the following balance for the given value of x?

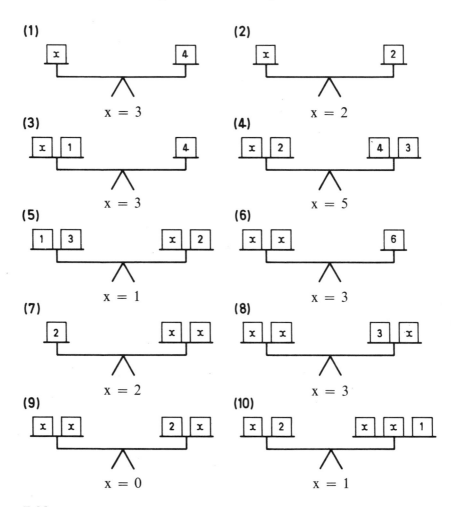

(1)

x = 3

(2)

x = 2

(3)

x = 3

(4)

x = 5

(5)

x = 1

(6)

x = 3

(7)

x = 2

(8)

x = 3

(9)

x = 0

(10)

x = 1

7.22
Which of the equations given below are balanced for the given value of x?

(1) x = 5 when x = 2   (2) x + 6 = 9 when x = 2
(3) x + 3 = 5 when x = 2   (4) 2x = 8 when x = 4
(5) 2x + 1 = 5 when x = 2   (6) 3x + 2 = 5 when x = 1
(7) 2x = x + 3 when x = 3   (8) 4 + x = 3x when x = 1
(9) 5x + 1 = 16 when x = 3   (10) 4x + 2 = 3x when x = 2.

120

In 7.18, 7.19, and 7.20 you were writing down the equations of the balances and then finding a value for x. In other words, you were solving the equation.

A large part of mathematics is concerned with equations. An equation is the mathematician's shorthand for particular situations. It might represent a balance or a chemical reaction, a man's wages or an atomic explosion, in fact almost anything and everything can be expressed as an equation. Equations are, then, a mathematician's model of a real thing; it is necessary therefore to be able to solve equations. Some are easy to solve, some very difficult, and mathematicians have found a few which are still not solved after hundreds of years of trying.

In the remainder of this chapter we are going to look more closely at equations to see how we can solve them without having to use a balance.

7.24
If we have the equation: $x + 3 = 4$.
What is the value of x?
You probably said straight away $x = 1$.
Another way of looking at it might have been as follows. The balance for this equation is:

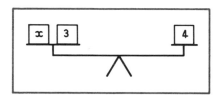

If we remove the | 3 | from the left-hand side, we are left with

| x | on the left and | 4 | on the right.

What must be done to restore the balance? Remember the golden rule we developed in 7.16.

If we now take | 3 | from the right-hand side, balance is restored.

We are left with $x = 1$.
Look at the following examples:
Example 1 $x + 5 = 8$

5

The balance would be:

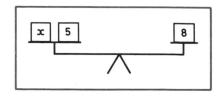

What do we take from the left-hand side to leave only x?
What do we take from the right-hand side to restore balance?
What is the value of x?
You should have x = 3.
Example 2   x + 7 = 15
Try answering the following without drawing a balance.
What do we take from the left-hand side to leave only x?
What do we take from the right-hand side to restore balance?
What is the value of x?
You should have x = 8.
Example 3   11 = x + 4
Try answering the following without using a balance.
Which side of the equation is x on?
What must be taken away to leave x on its own?
What must be done to restore balance?
What is the value of x?
You should have 7 = x or x = 7.
Example 4   17 = x + 9
We need to take 9 from the right-hand side to leave x on its own.
To keep balance we must remove 9 from the other side, so:
17 = x + 9.
Take 9 from both sides: 8 = x.
The value of x is 8 or x = 8.

7.25
Use the method developed above to solve the following equations;
your work should be laid out as in the example above.

(1) x + 1 = 4	(2) x + 3 = 11
(3) x + 7 = 14	(4) x + 8 = 12
(5) 16 = x + 2	(6) 19 = x + 7
(7) x + 5 = 5	(8) x + 1 = 7 + 3.

7.26
How are we going to solve equations of the sort 2x = 6?
Can we take something from both sides as we did before?
Think carefully about this.

Let us look at the balance:

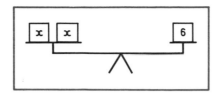

We have from the balance: x + x = 6.
Is there anything we can take from both sides?
Can we take x from both sides?
Can we take 6 from both sides?
Does this help us to find the value of x?
So for the equation x + x = 6 or 2x = 6 there is nothing that we can take from both sides to obtain a solution set.
How does the above equation differ from x + 2 = 6? (Here we can take something from both sides.)
As there is nothing that can be taken from both sides, what are we to do?
We know that the left-hand side consists of two equal parts, i.e., x + x or 2x. Can we then split the right-hand side into two equal parts, i.e., can we split 6 into two equal parts?
We now get:

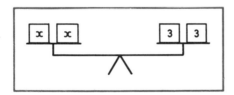

So we see that x = 3.
Look at the following examples:
Example 1   3x = 6
Is there anything we can take from both sides?
If not, why not?
How many equal parts are there on the left-hand side?
Can the right-hand side be divided into three equal parts?

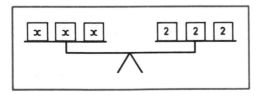

So from 3x = 6 we get x = 2.

Example 2   4x = 8
What can we take from both sides?
Nothing.
How many equal parts are there on the left-hand side?
Will the right-hand side split into the same number of equal parts?
What value does this give for x?
You should have x = 2.
Example 3   3x = 7
The left-hand side has three equal parts.
7 will not divide into three equal parts such that each part ∈ N
(Do you remember what set N stands for? You met it in chapter 2.)
So 3x = 7 cannot be solved for x ∈ N. (There is, however, a solution
to this equation which is not an element of N.)
Example 4   3x + x = 8
What does the left-hand side mean?
Look at the balance:

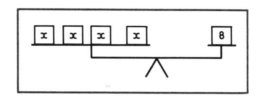

We have 4x on the left, i.e., 3x + x = 4x, so 3x + x = 8 becomes
4x = 8.
Four equal parts are required so: x = 2.

7.27
Use the method developed above to solve the following equations
(x ∈ N). Your work should be laid out as neatly as possible with
each step on a new line.

(1) 2x = 2	(2) 2x = 10	(3) 2x = 18
(4) 3x = 12	(5) 3x = 3	(6) 3x = 15
(7) 5x = 15	(8) 4x = 16	(9) 6 = 3x
(10) 20 = 10x	(11) x + x = 4	(12) 2x + 2x = 8
(13) 5x + x = 6	(14) 3x + 5x = 24	(15) 8 + 6 = 4x + 3x.

7.28
We have seen how to solve equations such as: x + 7 = 9
and also: 2x = 2.
How will we solve: 2x + 7 = 9?
Use a sketch of a balance to help you. (We have here a mixture of
the two types of equation that we have already met.)

Here is an example: $3x + 2 = 8$.
The balance would be:

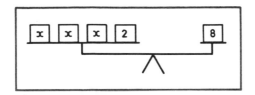

We can remove 2 from both sides of the balance to give: $3x = 6$.
Splitting both sides into three equal parts we get: $x = 2$.
Now solve the same equation without using a balance. $3x + 2 = 8$.
Take 2 from both sides: $3x = 6$.
Dividing both sides into three equal parts: $x = 2$.
Your working of 7.28 should have been something like this:
The equation was $2x + 7 = 9$.
Take 7 from both sides: $2x = 2$.
Divide both sides into two equal parts: $x = 1$.

7.30
Using the methods developed above, solve the following equations,
using a similar layout to that in 7.29.
(1) $2x + 2 = 4$ (2) $2x + 3 = 7$ (3) $3x + 7 = 10$
(4) $3x + 2 = 11$ (5) $5x + 1 = 16$ (6) $8 = 2x + 2$
(7) $2x + 4 = 7 + 3$ (8) $3x + 2 = 10 + 1$ (9) $3x + 2x + 4 = 9$.

7.31
The last type of equation we are going to look at is: $2x = 3 + x$.
How do we solve this?
A balance may help:

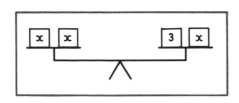

Is there anything we can take from both sides?
What is left?
What is the value of x?
You should have $x = 3$.

7.32   *Example 1*   5x = 3x + 2.

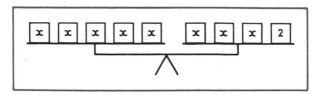

We can take 3x from both sides, leaving 2x = 2.
Dividing both sides into two equal parts gives: x = 1.
Example 2   3x + 2x = 4x + 1
becomes: 5x = 4x + 1
Taking 4x from both sides: x = 1.

7.32
Solve the following equations:
(1) 2x = x + 3   (2) 2x = x + 7   (3) 3x = x + 4
(4) 3x = 5 + 2x   (5) 2x + 4 = 6x   (6) 8x = 5x + 6
(7) 12 + 3x = 9x   (8) 8x + 3x = 5x + 6 (9) 7 + 3x = 8x + 2x.

7.33
Notice how in *every* equation we have dealt with in this chapter we
have used *one* rule which is the same each time.
    If we take something from one side we must take the same from
the other side;
    If we divide one side by something then we must divide the other
side into the same number of parts. In other words: *what we do to
one side, we must do to the other*.
This is the golden rule of equations.

7.34
Solve the following equations.
Remember at all times the golden rule.
The solutions should all be elements of N.
    (1) x + 3 = 7   (2) 3 + x = 10
    (3) x + 4 = 5 + 3   (4) 8 = 4 + x
    (5) 12 = x + 9   (6) 2x = 6
    (7) 18 = 6x   (8) 12 + 3 = 5x
    (9) 9 + 7 = 4x   (10) 2x + 3 = 9
  (11) 3x + 5 = 8   (12) 8 = 2x + 2
  (13) 11 = 5x + 1   (14) 5x + 2x = 21
  (15) 18 = 5x + 4x   (16) 3 + 13 = 3x + x
  (17) 5x = 2 + 3x   (18) 3x = 8 + 2x
  (19) 2x + 8 = 4x   (20) 2x + 8 = 4x + 2
  (21) 3 + 3x = 5 + 2x   (22) 5 + 2x = 3 + 4x.

I think of a number, add 2, and the answer is 7; what was the number?

Can you write the above statement in a mathematical form? (Let x stand for the number.)

Write down an equation for each of the following statements and then solve the equation.

(1) I think of a number, add 7, and the answer is 15.

(2) I think of a number, multiply it by 2, and the answer is 12.

(3) I think of a number, multiply it by 3, add 2, and the answer is 5.

(4) Tom has 3 times as many marbles as Peter; together they have 24 marbles. (As a start let Peter have x marbles.)

Interest page

Number patterns

(1) The following set is the set of multiples of 9 in base ten
{9, 18, 27, 36, 45, 54, 63, 72, 81, 90, ---}. You may have noticed a
pattern in this set of multiples that does not occur in any other set
of multiples in base ten. Add the digits in each number in the set:

for 9 we have 9   for 18 we have $1 + 8 =$

for 27 we have $2 + 7 =$ for 36 we have $3 + 6 =$

(2) The following set of multiples contains the multiples of 4 in base
five {4, 13, 22, 31, 40, ---}. Adding the digits:

for 4 we have 4   for 13 we have $1 + 3 =$

for 22 we have $2 + 2 =$ for 31 we have $3 + 1 =$

Compare this pattern with that for the previous set of multiples in
base ten. Can you see any similarity?
The two sets were:

(1) the set of multiples of 9 in base *ten*

(2) the set of multiples of 4 in base *five*.

(3) Look at the following sets of multiples and see if the same
pattern exists in them:

> {6, 15, 24, 33, 42, 51, 60, ---}
> the set of multiples of 6 in base *seven*
> {5, 14, 23, 32, 41, 50, ---}
> the set of multiples of 5 in base *six*.

(4) Write down the set of multiples of 7 in base eight. Does the same
pattern exist?

(5) In the set of multiples of 9 in base ten the next two members of
this set are 99 and 108. These are the eleventh and twelfth members
of the set. Notice that the eleventh member of the set does not, at
first, appear to fit the pattern. We can, however, get over this problem by saying that we go on adding the digits until we get a single
digit number.

For 99 we say $9 + 9 = 18$ and for 18, $1 + 8 = 9$.

(6) Write down the next two terms in the other sets of multiples and
see if this problem occurs in them also.

For example, for the set of multiples of 4 in base five, write down
the sixth and seventh terms.

For the set of multiples of 6 in base seven, write down the eighth and ninth terms, etc.

(7) What set of multiples in base n forms a similar pattern to the other ones in this question?

(8) What is the first term in the previous series (in terms of n) whose digits must be added up twice, to fit the pattern?

8. From ordered pairs to graphs

In chapter 5 we gave addresses to the squares in a composition table. This technique is used in street directories and map references like the one shown below.

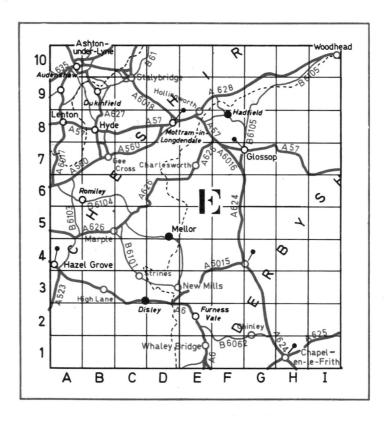

8.1
In the map Mellor can be found quite easily by referring to its grid reference D, 5. This could be written in the form of an ordered pair (D, 5), where the x value ∈ {A, B, C, D, E, ---, I} and the y value ∈ {1, 2, 3, 4, ---, 10}.

8.2
Write down the map references (in the form of an ordered pair) of the following places on the above map:

8.3

(1) Hazel Grove	(2) Mottram-in-Longdendale
(3) Chinley	(4) Dukinfield
(5) Whaley Bridge	(6) Glossop
(7) Chapel-en-le-Frith	(8) High Lane
(9) Charlesworth	(10) Ashton-under-Lyne
(11) Stalybridge	(12) Marple.

8.3

Give the names of the places with the following map references:

(1) (A, 8)   (2) (E, 2)   (3) (B, 8)
(4) (I, 10)   (5) (A, 9)   (6) (C, 3).

8.4

The system of ordered pairs which we have used so far is adequate when we wish to refer to squares, but when we wish to refer to points our system does not always give us the necessary information. For example, the map reference (C, 3) refers both to Disley and Strines, because they belong to the same square.

If we wish to distinguish between two points we must modify our system.

8.5

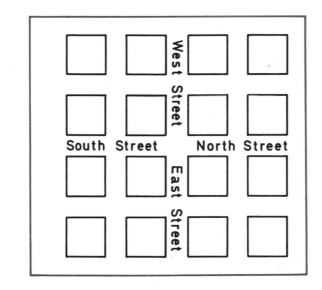

(1)

Diagram (1) above shows a plan of a modern town based on a rectangular lattice. Many examples of this can be found in America, but very few in Britain. This is because British towns and cities have never been built systematically but have developed slowly over a period of many years. Two examples of this plan can, however, be found in the British Isles. One of these in the West Riding of York-shire is called Saltaire. It is situated in the heart of the woollen industry. Sir Titus Salt, a wealthy mill owner, built the village in the nineteenth century for the people working in his mills.

The other example can be found in the north of Scotland. It is a small fishing village called Ullapool and was built by Thomas Telford in the early part of the nineteenth century. You could find any place in such a city by a system of ordered pairs. The ordered pairs used in this case are called *cartesian co-ordinates*.

Diagram (2) illustrates another method of planning a city. It shows the Arc de Triomphe in Paris and again any place in the locality can be found by using a different kind of ordered pair called *polar co-ordinates*.

(2)

8.6

To give any square in the previous work an address, we need two numbers. (This was a two-dimensional figure.)

(1) How many numbers do we need to give an address to a point on a line (which is a one-dimensional figure)?

(2) How many numbers do we need to give an address to a point in a three-dimensional figure?

8.7

Write down the addresses of the following points shown on the number line.

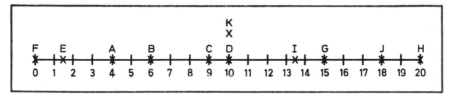

(1) A   (2) B   (3) C   (4) D   (5) E
(6) F   (7) G   (8) H   (9) I   (10) J.
(11) What is unusual about the addresses of the points E and I?
(12) What would the address of the point K be? Note that it must be different from that of D.

8.8

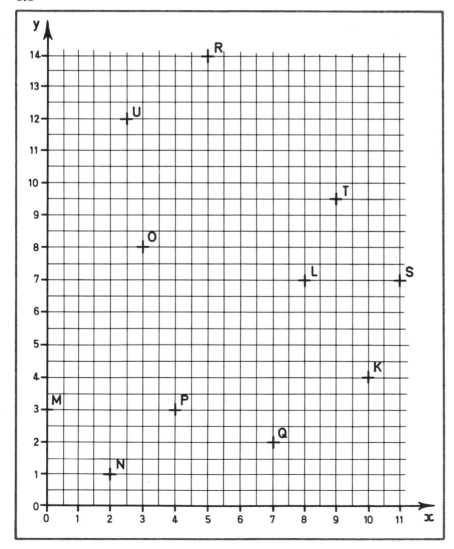

8.9

Two different points cannot have the same address, just as two different squares cannot have the same address in our previous system. It is obvious that if we are to give K an address we need another number in the address, because we have moved off the one-dimensional line into two dimensions again and we are back to the ordered pair. Consequently we must add another number line (or axis) so that we can give K another number in its address, to refer to its vertical distance from the first axis. Notice that the numbers on the axes now refer to the lines only and not to the spaces between them. The ordered pair for K is thus (10, 4).

8.9

(1) Write the address of the following points on the grid of 8.8 in the form of an ordered pair (x, y):

(a) L   (b) M   (c) N   (d) O   (e) P
(f) Q   (g) R   (h) S   (i) T   (j) U

(2) What is unusual about the y value of the point T and the x value of the point U?

Now that we are considering points instead of squares on our squared lattice, we have had to form our ordered pairs from a different set of numbers. For the addresses of squares we used the set of natural numbers plus nought, i.e., {0, 1, 2, 3, 4, –––}, but for the addresses of points we have had to add on the set of fractions. The new set is called the set of *rational numbers* which is composed of the natural numbers together with nought, and the fractions.

8.10

(1) Plot the following set of points on graph paper:

$$\{(0, 5), (1, 4), (2\tfrac{1}{2}, 2\tfrac{1}{2}), (3, 2), (3\tfrac{1}{2}, 1\tfrac{1}{2}), (4, 1), (5, 0)\}.$$

(2) Do they form a pattern?

(3) If they do form a simple pattern, then there must be an equation in x and y that will describe the pattern so that all the ordered pairs will balance. Can you find this equation? Try adding the x and y values of the points:

(a) $0 + 5 =$ (b) $1 + 4 =$
(c) $2\tfrac{1}{2} + 2\tfrac{1}{2} =$ (d) $3 + 2 =$
(e) $3\tfrac{1}{2} + 1\tfrac{1}{2} =$ (f) $4 + 1 =$
(g) $5 + 0 =$ (h) $x + y =$

(4) Does the point $(4\tfrac{1}{2}, \tfrac{1}{2})$ belong to this set? It was not included in the original set, but it does fit our equation because $4\tfrac{1}{2} + \tfrac{1}{2} = 5$. Plot this point on the same graph paper.

(5) Write down three more ordered pairs which fit the equation $x + y = 5$. Plot these points on your graph and compare your results with your neighbour. How many points will fit the equation $x + y = 5$?

(6) Obviously our original set of ordered pairs is part of a much greater set. How could you represent the whole set of ordered pairs on your graph?

8.11

It is impossible to list all the ordered pairs that fit the equation $x + y = 5$, so we have to find some other way of describing this set and we write: $\{(x, y)/x + y = 5\}$ which reads 'the set of ordered pairs (x, y) such that the sum of x and y is 5'.
Write down the meanings of the following:
(1) $\{(x, y)/x + y = 7\}$
(2) $\{(x, y)/x - y > 4\}$
(3) $\{(x, y)/x + y < 2\}$.

8.12

Do the following ordered pairs belong to $\{(x, y)/x + y = 5\}$? If you are not sure, plot the points on your graph and see if they belong to the pattern formed by this set.

(1) $(1, 7)$	(2) $(\frac{1}{2}, 4\frac{1}{2})$	(3) $(6, 1)$
(4) $(0, 8)$	(5) $(2\frac{1}{4}, 2\frac{3}{4})$	(6) $(1\frac{1}{2}, 3\frac{1}{2})$
(7) $(10, 1)$	(8) $(3\frac{1}{5}, 1\frac{4}{5})$	(9) $(2\frac{1}{2}, 4\frac{1}{2})$.

8.13

Which of the following statements are true?
(1) $(2, 4) \in \{(x, y)/x + y = 6\}$
(2) $(2\frac{1}{2}, 4\frac{1}{2}) \in \{(x, y)/y - x = 2\}$
(3) $(2, 4) \in \{(x, y)/y = 2x\}$
(4) $(3, 5) \in \{(x, y)/y + x = 6\}$
(5) $(2, 7) \in \{(x, y)/y - x = 5\}$
(6) $(3, 15) \in \{(x, y)/y + x = 18\}$
(7) $(1\frac{3}{4}, 5\frac{1}{4}) \in \{(x, y)/x + y = 7\}$
(8) $(1\frac{1}{2}, 7\frac{1}{2}) \in \{(x, y)/x + y = 8\}$
(9) $(\frac{3}{4}, 2\frac{1}{4}) \in \{(x, y)/x + y = 3\}$
(10) $(7\frac{3}{4}, 3\frac{3}{4}) \in \{(x, y)/x - y = 4\}$.

8.14

In 8.12 the ordered pairs of points that do not lie on the line $x + y = 5$ all lie on one side of the line and for these points:

$1 + 7 > 5$	$6 + 1 > 5$
$0 + 8 > 5$	$10 + 1 > 5$
$2\frac{1}{2} + 4\frac{1}{2} > 5$	$3 + 2\frac{1}{2} > 5.$

(1) Can you suggest a generalization that will describe the set of all ordered pairs where the sum of the x and y values is greater than five?

135

(2) Shade this set in on your graph and label it with the generalization.

8.15

(1) Where will the set of points $\{(x, y)/x + y < 5\}$ lie on your graph?

(2) Write down three points whose ordered pairs belong to this set.

8.16

Your graph is now divided into three distinct sets of points. They are:

$A = \{(x, y)/x + y = 5\}$
$B = \{(x, y)/x + y > 5\}$
$C = \{(x, y)/x + y < 5\}$.

Label the areas A, B, and C on your graph.

Write down to which set (A, B, or C) the following belong:

(1) $(1, 9)$ (2) $(2, 3)$ (3) $(1, 3)$

(4) $(1\frac{1}{2}, 2)$ (5) $(3\frac{1}{2}, 1\frac{1}{2})$ (6) $(9\frac{1}{2}, 6\frac{1}{2})$

(7) $(\frac{1}{2}, 4)$ (8) $(1\frac{3}{4}, 2\frac{1}{4})$ (9) $(5\frac{1}{4}, 3)$.

8.17

A conversion graph allows us to convert data from one set of units into another. For example, if we were going to Spain we would need to convert pounds into pesetas or vice versa, we could draw a conversion graph to help us.

Five pounds is approximately equivalent to eight hundred pesetas and, of course, no pounds is equivalent to no pesetas. Since we only need two points to draw a line we can draw a conversion graph from this data. If we make the horizontal axis the pounds axis and the vertical axis the pesetas axis, we can form ordered pairs from the above data, thus $A = (5, 800)$, $B = (0, 0)$ where the first figure refers to the horizontal axis and the second to the vertical axis. Look at the graph opposite where the two points A and B have been plotted. If we want to convert 1200 pesetas to pounds we look for a point on the line whose vertical co-ordinate (in the ordered pair) is 1200 and read off the corresponding horizontal co-ordinate from the pounds axis. Such a point is C. The corresponding horizontal co-ordinate of the ordered pairs is $7\frac{1}{2}$. Thus C has an ordered pair of $(7\frac{1}{2}, 1200)$, therefore, £7·50 are equivalent to 1200 pesetas.

To convert 400 pesetas to pounds we find the point D on the line whose vertical co-ordinate is 400 and read off its horizontal co-ordinate from the pounds axis. Thus the co-ordinates of $D = (2\frac{1}{2}, 400)$ tell us that 400 pesetas are equivalent to £2·50.

To convert 8 pounds to pesetas we find the point E on the line

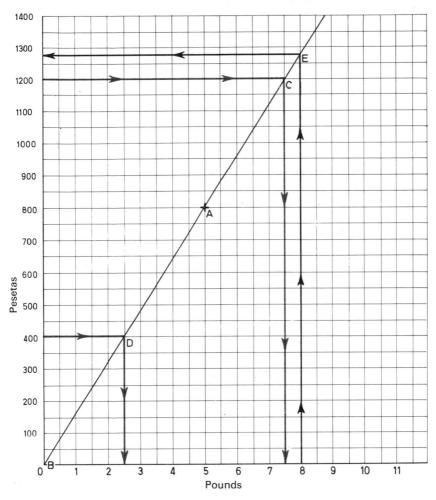

Conversion graph for pounds and pesetas.

whose horizontal co-ordinate is 8 and read off its vertical co-ordinate from the pesetas axis. Thus E = (8, 1280) and, therefore, 8 pounds are equivalent to 1280 pesetas.

Use the graph to convert the following:

(1) 500 pesetas to pounds
(2) 2 pounds to pesetas
(3) 6 pounds to pesetas
(4) 1150 pesetas to pounds.

8.18 Recall

(1) Write down the equations of the following sets of ordered pairs:

(a) $\{(0, 10), (1, 9), (2, 8), (3, 7), (4, 6), (\frac{1}{2}, 9\frac{1}{2}), ---\}$

(b) $\{(6, 6), (7, 5), (4, 8), (9, 3), (2, 10), ---\}$

(c) $\{(5, 4), (3, 6), (7, 2), (4, 5), (8, 1), ---\}$

(d) $\{(\frac{1}{2}, 5\frac{1}{2}), (1, 5), (4\frac{1}{2}, 1\frac{1}{2}), (3\frac{3}{4}, 2\frac{1}{4}), ---\}$

(e) $\{(10, 4), (7, 1), (8, 2), (17, 11), (12, 6), (6\frac{1}{2}, \frac{1}{2}), ---\}$

(f) $\{(12, 8), (10, 6), (6, 2), (4\frac{1}{2}, \frac{1}{2}), (13, 9), (14, 10), ---\}$

(g) $\{(2, 4), (3, 2), (4, 0), (0, 8), (1, 6), (2\frac{1}{2}, 3), (1\frac{1}{2}, 5), ---\}$

(h) $\{(10, 0), (1, 4\frac{1}{2}), (3, 3\frac{1}{2}), (5, 2\frac{1}{2}), (2, 4), (4, 3), ---\}$

(i) $\{(2, 8), (5, 11), (3, 9), (12, 18), (24, 30), (13, 19), ---\}$

(j) $\{(1, 4\frac{1}{2}), (2, 3), (4, 0), (0, 6), (2\frac{1}{2}, 2\frac{1}{4}), ---\}$.

(2) List five members of each of the following sets and plot them on graph paper:

(a) $\{(x, y)/x + y = 8\}$ call this set A

(b) $\{(x, y)/x + y = 11\}$ call this set B

(c) $\{(x, y)/x - y = 4\}$ call this set C.

(3) Two lines cross in one point:

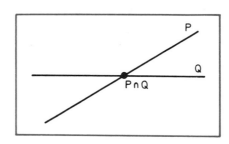

The point where the lines cross is the intersection of the two sets of points P and Q. Write down the intersections of the sets A, B, and C of (2) in the form of an ordered pair (x, y).

(a) $A \cap C = \{ \ \}$ (b) $B \cap C = \{ \ \}$ (c) $A \cap B = \{ \ \}$.

Be careful with the last one, it is a special set.

(4) Plot the following sets of points on the same axes:

(a) $\{(0, 3), (1, 3), (5, 3), (15, 3), (12, 3), (4, 3), ---\}$

another way of describing this set is $\{(x, y)/y = 3\}$

(b) $\{(5, 4), (5, 0), (5, 10), (5, 3), (5, 2), (5, 1), (5, 6), (5, 7), ---\}$

another way of describing this set is $\{(x, y)/x = 5\}$.

(5) (a) On the same graph as you used for (4) shade in the following sets:

$A = \{(x, y)/y > 3\}$ shade this set: ▨

$B = \{(x, y)/x > 5\}$ shade this set: ▨

(b) How would you describe the set of points shaded ▢ ?

(6) (a) On another set of axes shade in the following sets:

$A = \{(x, y)/y > 2\}$ shade this set: ▤

$B = \{(x, y)/y < 7\}$ shade this set: ▥

(b) Where is the set $A \cap B$ on the axes? How is it shaded?

(c) Describe the set $A \cap B$ in the form $\{(x, y)/ \quad \}$.

(7) (a) Shade in the following sets of points on another piece of graph paper: $\{(x, y)/x < 4\}$ and $\{(x, y)/x > 10\}$.

(b) Describe the part of the graph left unshaded in the form $\{(x, y)/ \quad \}$.

(8) Plot the following pairs of points on graph paper and join them up. Find the mid point of each line joining the two original points. Is there any way of obtaining the mid point without plotting any points?
(a) (0, 2) and (10, 4)   (b) (4, 8) and (2, 2)
(c) (3, 4) and (7, 6)   (d) (1, 9) and (0, 1)
(e) (13, 2) and (2, 4).

(9) Without plotting any points, write down the mid points of the lines joining the following pairs of points.
(a) (11, 2) and (1, 12)   (b) (256, 12) and (254, 14)
(c) (131, 6) and (1, 14)   (d) (21, 13) and (22, 14)
(e) (6, 5) and (122, 2).

(10) Draw a conversion graph for metres and kilometres, taking the horizontal axis for metres and the vertical axis for kilometres. We know that one thousand metres are equivalent to one kilometre and also that no metres are equivalent to no kilometres. Thus we have two ordered pairs (1000, 1) and (0, 0). Plot these on your graph and draw the line which passes through them. Use a scale of five millimetres to one hundred metres on the metres axis and five centimetres to one kilometre on the kilometre axis.
Use your graph to convert the following distances:
(a) 500 m to km (b) 1850 m to km (c) 205 m to km
(d) $1\frac{3}{10}$ km to m (e) $\frac{7}{10}$ km to m (f) 0·35 km to m
(g) Find the dimensions of your classroom in metres and use your graph to convert the measurements to kilometres.

(11) In a certain examination, the total number of marks possible is 75; this is to be equivalent to marks out of 100 (100 per cent); no marks being equivalent to no per cent. Draw a conversion graph for marks out of 75 and equivalent marks out of a hundred.
Use your graph to convert the following marks out of 75 to marks out of 100:
(a) 25 (b) 50 (c) 70 (d) 5 (e) 35 (f) 44
What were the scores out of 75 of pupils who scored the following percentages:
(g) 10 (h) 70 (i) 20 (j) 42 (k) 53 (l) 37?
Give your answers to the nearest whole number.

(12) The conversion rate for British and American currency is approximately twenty-four dollars to ten pounds. Using this information, draw a conversion graph of dollars to pounds and use it to convert the following:
(a) £8 to dollars   (b) £2·50 to dollars
(c) 80p to dollars   (d) 20$ to pounds
(e) 5$ to pounds   (f) 13$ to pounds

(13) In running an eight hundred metre race, an athlete has to complete two laps of a race track. Using this information, draw a conversion graph of laps to metres and use it to convert the following:

(a) 100 *m* to laps   (b) 1500 *m* to laps

(c) 10,000 *m* to laps   (d) $12\frac{1}{2}$ laps to metres

(e) $7\frac{1}{2}$ laps to metres

Interest page

Experiment 1

(1) On a sheet of graph paper plot the following sets of ordered pairs and join them up as stated:

(a) {(2, 6), (2, 8), (3, 5), (3, 7), (4, 6), (4, 8), (5, 5), (5, 7)}

Join: (2, 6) to (2, 8), (3, 5), and (4, 6)

      (2, 8) to (4, 8) and (3, 7)

      (5, 7) to (3, 7), (4, 8), and (5, 5)

      (5, 5) to (3, 5) and (4, 6)

      (4, 6) to (4, 8)

      (3, 7) to (3, 5).

(b) {(7, 8), (7, 9), (8, 10), (8, 7), (9, 8), (9, 9)}

Join: (8, 7) to (7, 8), (8, 10), and (9, 8)

      (8, 10) to (7, 9) and (9, 9).

(c) {(9, 6), (9, 11), (10, 7), (10, 10), (11, 6), (11, 11)}

Join: (10, 7) to (9, 6), (11, 6), and (10, 10)

      (10, 10) to (9, 11) and (11, 11).

The figures in (a), (b) and (c) are well known examples of optical illusions. Describe these illusions and find out as much as you can about other examples of optical illusion. There are many examples in the world of modern art. Collect examples with descriptions and make up wall charts.

Experiment 2

On another sheet of graph paper plot the following sets of ordered pairs and join them up as stated:

(a) {(1, 1), (3, 1), (3, 2), (2, 2), (2, 3), (1, 3)}

Join: (1, 1) to (3, 1)

      (3, 1) to (3, 2)

      (3, 2) to (2, 2)

      (2, 2) to (2, 3)

      (2, 3) to (1, 3)

      (1, 3) to (1, 1).

(b) {(5, 1), (5, 2), (6, 3), (7, 3), (7, 2), (8, 2), (8, 1), (6, 2)}

Join: (5, 1) to (5, 2)

      (5, 2) to (6, 2)

      (6, 2) to (6, 3)

            (6, 3) to (7, 3)
            (7, 3) to (7, 2)
            (7, 2) to (8, 2)
            (8, 2) to (8, 1)
            (8, 1) to (5, 1).
(c) {(10, 2), (11, 3), (12, 2), (11, 1)}
Join: (10, 2) to (11, 3)
            (11, 3) to (12, 2)
            (12, 2) to (11, 1)
            (11, 1) to (10, 2).

If we take any one of the figures formed in (a), (b), and (c) it is possible to make a lot of identical figures and fit them together so that
they cover an area without leaving any gaps. Areas covered in this
way are called *tessellations*.

Experiment 3

The sets described in experiment 1 could not be joined up in a con-
tinuous way, i.e., could not be drawn without either taking the
pencil off the paper and starting at another point, or by going over
one line more than once. Whereas the sets in experiment 2(a), (b),
and (c) could be traced out continuously; investigate this problem.

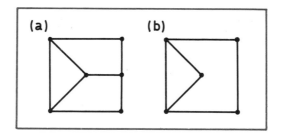

This diagram gives two more examples. Example (a) cannot be
traced, but example (b) can.

The problem has something to do with the points where the lines
meet. Call these points *nodes*. There are two types of node: (i) odd
nodes, where an odd number of lines meet, and (ii) even nodes,
where an even number of lines meet. Colour these nodes in two
distinctive colours in all the diagrams you draw. Keep your diagrams simple.

Further research

There are many different types of game played on boards of squares
or rectangular lattices. Some are played on the squares and some

are played on the lines. Some examples of such games are: Battleships and Cruisers; Draughts; Chess; Wei-chi (a Chinese game); Hnefatafl (a Saxon game).

Find out as much as you can about games played on these boards and compile a folder on them.

9. Playing with squares

Materials required
Straws of assorted lengths, some being very nearly equal in length;
pebbles of various sizes; cards of various shapes; and twelve
one-centimetre squares cut from card.

9.1

Arrange the straws in order of size. Carefully check the ones that
are nearly the same length. Discuss with your teacher how you can
be sure that straws that are nearly the same length are put in the
right place.
Starting with the shortest, measure and write down the length of
each straw.
(1) What units have you used to compare the lengths of the straws?
(2) What other units of length do we use?
(3) Find out about units of length and the ways of comparing
lengths used by (a) other countries, (b) people in this country 500 to
600 years ago, and (c) people like the Ancient Greeks and the
Romans. Your teacher will be able to recommend books. (Try
encyclopaedias and magazines like *Knowledge*.)

9.2

Arrange the pebbles in order of size. How can you check that you
are right? With the straws you could measure the length, do you
think it would be any use measuring the length of the pebbles? See
what your friends think; see what your teacher thinks.
To compare the pebbles you must find out which is the heaviest.
You really need a pair of scales to compare their weights. Can you

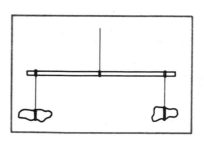

suggest a way of doing this without using proper scales? You could make a simple balance by using a stick and a piece of string:
This would show you which stones were the heavier. Check all your pebbles in this way.
If you can get some proper scales find out what the weights of your pebbles are; list the weights in order starting with the biggest.
(1) What units of weight have you been using?
(2) What other units of weight do we use in this country?
(3) Find out what units of weight are used in (a) other countries, (b) this country 500 to 600 years ago, and (c) in Ancient Greece and Rome.

9.3

Now take your set of cards and see if you can sort these into any order of size. You will find this a little more difficult. Can you compare them by measuring lengths? Can you compare them by measuring weights? How then? Discuss this problem with your friends. Remember the work we were doing in chapter 3 and see if you can use any of the ideas there to help you to solve this problem. Discuss your findings with your teacher. Now number your cards 1, 2, 3, 4, ––– and then write down which is the largest, which next, and so on.

9.4

Discuss the following statements with your teacher:
(1) John says that he is heavier than Bill. How can this be checked?
(2) Bill says that he has further to walk to school than Janet. How can this be checked?
(3) Jane was born in 1950 and Janet in 1951; who is the older?
(4) Pat says that she is bigger than Mary. What does this mean?
(5) How would you find which of these two vessels contains the most ink?

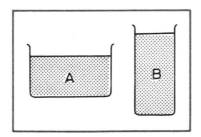

To check the truth of each of these statements we need a means of measurement. In (1) we should use kilogrammes to measure the two boys. Which units would you use in (2) and (3)?

Which units would you use to compare the following?

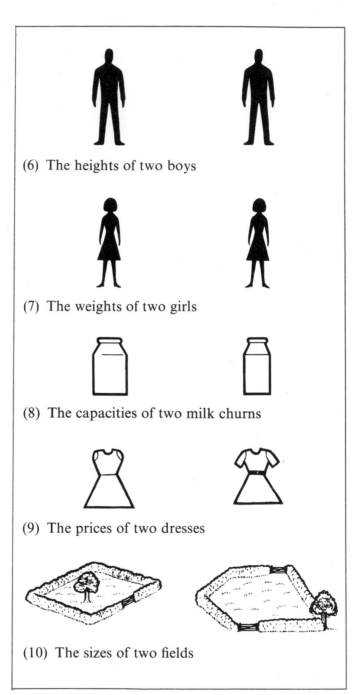

(6) The heights of two boys

(7) The weights of two girls

(8) The capacities of two milk churns

(9) The prices of two dresses

(10) The sizes of two fields

(12) How would you compare the sizes of these two figures?

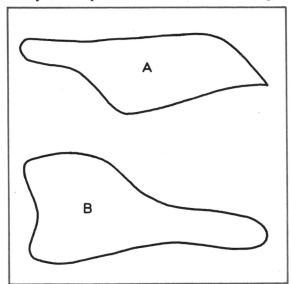

In our earlier work in chapter 3 we covered surfaces and figures like those above with triangles, circles, squares, rectangles, and other shapes. We found that surfaces like these could be covered with a pattern consisting of one of the shapes mentioned above. We could say that figure A needs five triangles or four circles to cover it, but would this be a satisfactory way of measuring the surface? Discuss with your friends which shape would be best to measure the figures A and B.

9.5
On a sheet of tracing paper draw a lattice on which the lines are one *cm* apart. Make your lattice about twelve centimetres long and eight centimetres wide. Now use this lattice to find the number of squares needed to cover the following shapes.

(1) **(a)**

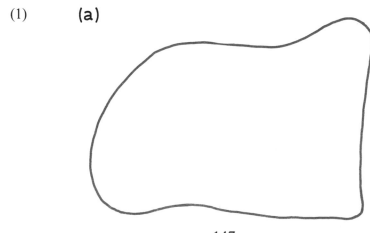

(b)

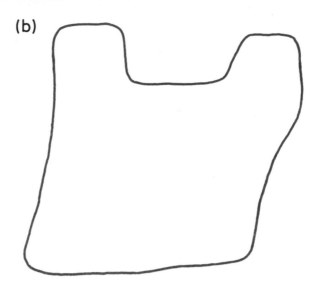

(2) In your atlas find a map of Great Britain and find out how many squares on your lattice are needed to cover it.

(3) Find the number of squares needed to cover the irregular shapes which your teacher will give you. The values you have obtained so far are only approximate since the square you have used is quite large compared with some of the shapes you have measured. How could we obtain a more accurate value for the measurement of a surface?

(4) Draw extra lines on your lattice so that the lines are five millimetres apart.

(5) How many five-millimetre squares are needed to exactly cover (a) a centimetre square, (b) a four-centimetre square, and (c) a ten-centimetre square?

Now find the number of centimetre squares needed to exactly cover each of the following shapes:

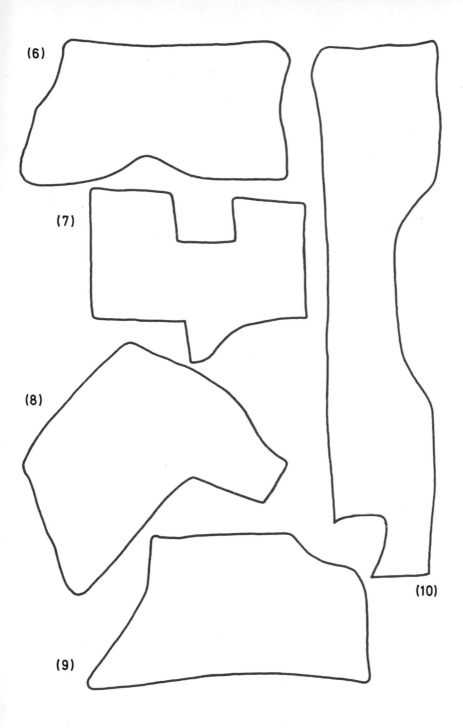

(6)

(7)

(8)

(9)

(10)

(11)   **(12)**

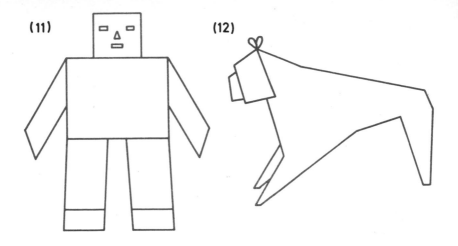

(13) List the shapes in (6) to (12) in order of size, using the answers you have obtained find the number of five millimetre squares needed to cover each of the figures.

This measure of a surface is normally called *the area of the surface*, the units we use are squares, with a side of one centimetre, one metre, or any other unit of length.

9.6

Using six of your one-centimetre squares, make up the following rectangles:

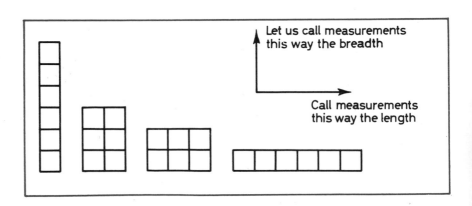

Let us call measurements this way the breadth

Call measurements this way the length

Copy and complete the following table:

Length	Breadth	Perimeter	Area (number of one-centimetre squares)
6	1	14	6
3			
	3		
1	6		6

Note: the length may sometimes be less than the breadth.

The perimeter of a rectangle is the distance around the edge.

Perimeter = AB + BC + CD + DA

    = 3 + 2 + 3 + 2

    = 10.

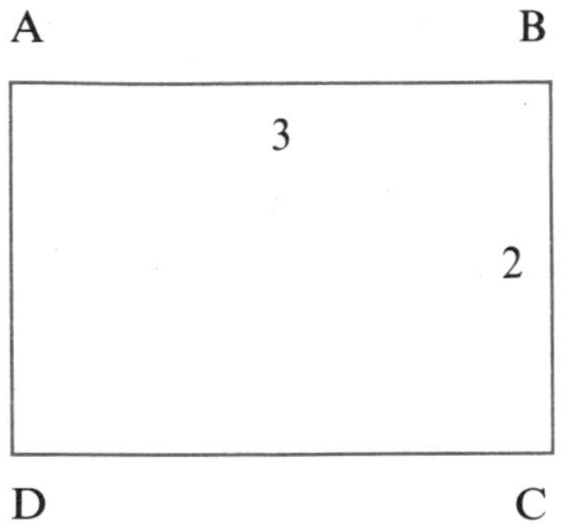

A   B

3

2

D   C

9.7

(1) Use your twelve one-centimetre squares to make as many different rectangles as you can; as you make them fill in the table below:

Length	Breadth	Perimeter	Area (number of one-centimetre squares)

(2) Using the table, plot on graph paper the breadth against the length for each rectangle you have formed.
Discuss the curve with your teacher.

(3) What do you notice about the area of each of the rectangles?

9.8

(1) A rectangle needs eight one-centimetre squares to cover it exactly. What could the length and breadth be? Put your answers in the table below:

Length	Breadth	Perimeter	Area (number of one-centimetre squares)
8	1		
4		12	
	4		
1			8

(2) A rectangle has a perimeter of thirty-six centimetres. Put the possible values of the length and breadth in the table below:

Length	Breadth	Perimeter	Area (number of one-centimetre squares)

(a) What do you notice about the area column?
(b) Plot on graph paper the area against the length.
Discuss the curve with your teacher.
(c) For what values of the length is the area greatest?
(d) What shape is the rectangle in this case?
(3) A rectangle needs sixty-four one-centimetre squares to cover it exactly.
(a) What is the shape of the rectangle when the perimeter has its smallest value?
(b) What is the area of this shape?
(4) How many one-centimetre squares are needed to cover rectangles with the following lengths and breadths:
(a) length 8 *cm*, breadth 6 *cm*
(b) length 10 *cm*, breadth 8 *cm*
(c) length 12 *cm*, breadth 12 *cm*.

(5) To save writing, we can put the numbers representing the length and breadth of a rectangle as an ordered pair like this (length, breadth). (10 *cm*, 6 *cm*) means that the length is 10 *cm* and the breadth is 6 *cm*.

(6) How many one-centimetre squares are needed to cover exactly the following rectangles:

(a) (4 *cm*, 3 *cm*)   (b) (5 *cm*, 4 *cm*)

(c) (7 *cm*, 9 *cm*)   (d) (10 *cm*, 12 *cm*)?

The number of one-centimetre squares needed to cover exactly a rectangle is called the area of the rectangle in square centimetres.

(7) What is the area of each of the following rectangles:

(a) (7 *cm*, 6 *cm*)   (b) (14 *cm*, 12 *cm*)

(c) (10 *cm*, 19 *cm*)   (d) (5 *cm*, 15 *cm*)?

(8) A rectangle is three metres long and two metres wide.

(a) How many one-metre squares are needed to exactly cover it?

(b) What is the area of the rectangle in square metres?

Square centimetres can be abbreviated to cm^2 (read as centimetres squared). Similarly, square metre can be abbreviated to m^2.

9.9

Find the area of each of the following shapes, the lengths are given in centimetres.

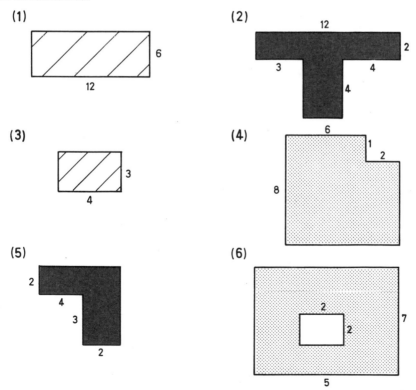

(7) A rectangle has a perimeter of 12 centimetres. What could the length and breadth be? Write your answers in shorthand form.

(8) A rectangle has a perimeter of 20 centimetres. The breadth b is 4 centimetres.

(a) What is the length l?

(b) What is the area?

(9) A rectangle has a perimeter of 24 centimetres.

(a) Fill in on the table below the possible values of the length, breadth, and area (l and $b \in$ N).

Length	Breadth	Area (square centimetres)

(b) For what value of the length and breadth is the area largest?

(c) What shape is the rectangle now?

(10) A farmer has 120 metres of fencing to make a rectangular sheep pen.

(a) What are the possible values of the length and breadth? (Work in multiples of ten only.)

Copy and complete the following table:

Length	Breadth	Area (square metres)

(b) What is the largest value of the area of the pen?

(c) What shape is the pen now?

(11) A rectangular lawn has a perimeter of 60 metres.
(a) List the possible values of the length, breadth, and area of the lawn. (Work in multiples of 5.)
(b) What is the largest area the lawn could have?
(c) Cut out from thin coloured card, rectangles to represent the different shapes of the lawn. (Cut at least five shapes.) On a sheet of card, draw axes and stick on your rectangles in order of size.
The diagram shows three of the cards in position.

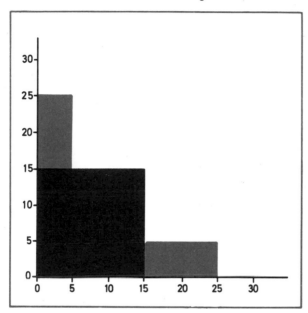

Join the tips of the rectangles with a line.
Look at the table for (11) again. We could write the length and breadth of our rectangle in the form of an ordered pair (length, breadth). If the length is 20 and the breadth is 10 we could write this as (20, 10).
(d) What does (12, 2) mean?
(e) What does (3, 8) mean?
The possible values of the length and breadth of the rectangles in (11) could now be written as a set in the form {(25, 5), (20, 10), (15, 15), (10, 20), (5, 25)}.
(12) The area of a rectangle is 36 square units; write the possible values of the length and breadth as a set, in the same way as it has been done above. One ordered pair in your set will be (4, 9). 36 is the result of multiplying 4 and 9. Cut from coloured card, rectangles to represent the different values of length and breadth. Stick these on axes as you did for (11). Discuss why you got a curved line for this question and a straight line for (11). The more rectangles you cut the better will be your curve.

(13) Repeat (12) for an area of 48 cm^2.

(14) Write down pairs of natural numbers which when multiplied give 72. Plot these pairs on graph paper.

(15) The area of a rectangle is 80 cm^2. Write down in set form the possible values of the length l and the breadth b. Call the set of values A.

This question could be worded as follows: 'Write down the members of the set A $= \{(l, b)/l \times b = 80, l$ and $b \in$ N$\}$'.

Discuss this way of writing the question with your teacher.

Solution:

Length	Breadth
80	1
40	2
20	4
16	5
10	8
8	10
5	16
4	20
2	40
1	80

So A $= \{(80, 1), (40, 2), (20, 4), (16, 5), (10, 8), (8, 10), (5, 16), (4, 20), (2, 40), (1, 80)\}$.

(16) Write down the members of the set:
$$B = \{(l, b)/l \times b = 96, l \text{ and } b \in N\}.$$

9.10 Recall

(1) A man wishes to lay a rectangular lawn of length 20 m and breadth 10 m. How many square metres of turf must he order?

(2) A kitchen is 3 m by 2 m.

(a) How many 25 cm square tiles are needed to cover the floor?

(b) If the tiles cost 4p each, what is the total cost of the tiles?

(3) A man wishes to lay a rectangular lawn 30 m by 10 m.

(a) What is the area of the lawn in square metres?

(b) If turf costs 10p per square metre, what is the cost of turfing the lawn?

(c) Seed costs 80p per kg. 1 kg of seed is enough for 20 m^2. How much seed is needed for the lawn to the nearest kilogramme?

(d) What would be the total cost of the seed?

(4) A room is 4 m long and 3 m wide. A man wishes to paint the ceiling, putting on two coats of paint. One litre of paint covers 14 m^2.

(a) How many litres of paint must he buy?

(b) If the paint costs 70*p* per litre, what is the cost of painting the ceiling?

(5) A farmer spreads fertilizer over his field at the rate of 60 *g* per square metre. How much fertilizer does he need for a 5009 m^2 field?

(6) How many one-centimetre squares are needed to cover this rectangle?

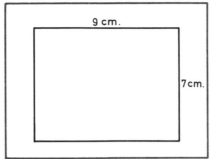

9 cm.

7cm.

(7) What is the length and the breadth of this rectangle?

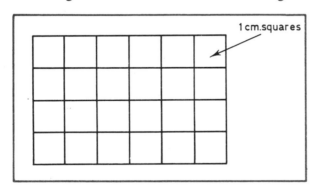

1 cm. squares

(8) Write down the possible values of the length and breadth of a rectangle if the area is 30 cm^2.

(9) Write down the possible values of the length, breadth, and area of a rectangle if the perimeter is 22 *cm*.

(10) Write down the members of:

(a) $A = \{(l, b)/l \times b = 16, l \text{ and } b \in N\}$

(b) $B = \{(l, b)/l + b = 9, l \text{ and } b \in N\}$.

(11) What is the shaded area of each of these figures? (The lengths are in metres.)

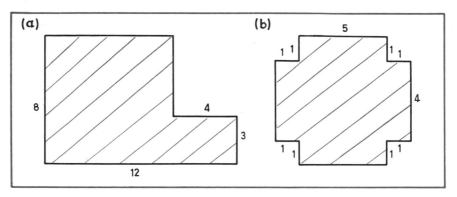

(12) Glass costs 70p per square metre; what is the total cost of replacing the following broken windows in a school:
(a) one window 3 m by 2 m   (b) one window 3·5 m × 4 m
(c) one window 4 m by 3 m   (d) one window 1·5 m × 2 m?
(13) If the area of a square is 25 cm², what is the length and the breadth?
(14) What is the shaded area?

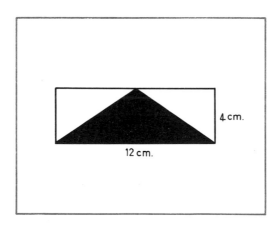

Interest page

Areas

Cut three of your one-centimetre squares in this way:

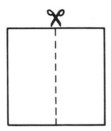

Two in this way:

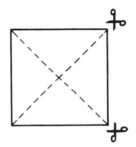

Now use these new shapes and the remaining squares to make these two figures:

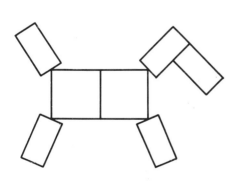 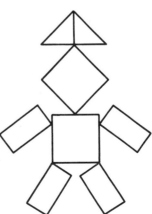

What is the area of each figure?
Make some other figures of your own and find their areas.

10. Smaller than one, and other fractions

10.1

Do you remember the name we gave earlier to the set of numbers $\{1, 2, 3, 4, 5, ---\}$? These were the numbers we used when counting the number of exercise books in a satchel or the number of desks in a room. Can they be used when we wish to describe how much cake we had for tea yesterday, or how much tart we ate at lunch today? If you had school dinner, did you have a whole tart to yourself? You probably found that the tart was already cut into eight parts when you collected it from the serving hatch.

Your share of the tart would be one part from the eight parts on the plate or $\frac{1}{8}$ of the tart. If someone on the table did not like the tart, you may have had two parts from the eight parts on the plate or $\frac{2}{8}$ of the tart. Notice the way in which we write the statement two parts from eight parts, i.e., $\frac{2}{8}$.

If two people on your table did not like the tart, then you might have had three parts of the eight parts on the plate or $\frac{3}{8}$ of the tart. The new numbers we have formed are called fractions; notice that they are formed from two members of N. The top part is called the numerator and the bottom the denominator;

$$\frac{3}{8} \begin{array}{l} \leftarrow \textit{numerator} \\ \leftarrow \textit{denominator} \end{array}$$

The denominator tells us how many parts the tart has been cut into and the numerator the number of parts you ate.

Discuss with your teacher the origin of the words numerator and denominator.

10.2

Write the following statements as fractions. Some of them have a simpler form, can you find them?

(1) 5 parts from 8 parts	(2) 4 parts from 8 parts
(3) 1 part from 3 parts	(4) 2 parts from 3 parts
(5) 3 parts from 4 parts	(6) 2 parts from 5 parts
(7) 4 parts from 6 parts	(8) 5 parts from 5 parts
(9) 6 parts from 7 parts	(10) 1 part from 4 parts
(11) 4 parts from 11 parts	(12) 7 parts from 9 parts.

Describe in words what the following fractions mean:

(1) $\frac{4}{5}$　　　　(2) $\frac{3}{4}$　　　　(3) $\frac{2}{3}$　　　　(4) $\frac{1}{5}$　　　　(5) $\frac{6}{7}$

(6) $\frac{4}{9}$　　　　(7) $\frac{9}{10}$　　　　(8) $\frac{7}{9}$　　　　(9) $\frac{2}{5}$.

10.4

For each of these diagrams say:

(a) how many equal parts the shape is divided into

(b) how many parts are shaded

(c) what fraction of the shape is unshaded.

(1) 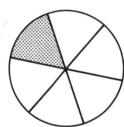　　　　**(2)**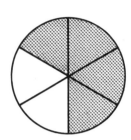

(3) 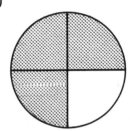　　　　**(4)**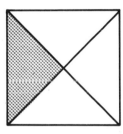

(5) 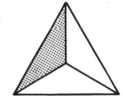　　　　**(6)**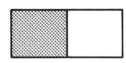

(7) 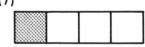　　　　**(8)**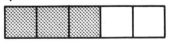

(9) 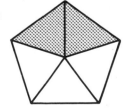　　　　**(10)**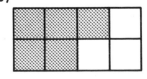

10.5

Draw small diagrams like those in 10.4, divide them into equal parts and then shade the appropriate number of parts to represent the following fractions:

(1) $\frac{1}{2}$ (2) $\frac{3}{4}$ (3) $\frac{2}{4}$

(4) $\frac{2}{5}$ (5) $\frac{1}{3}$ (6) $\frac{4}{7}$

(7) $\frac{3}{8}$ (8) $\frac{2}{9}$ (9) $\frac{4}{11}$.

10.6

Cut out, from card, rectangles of the following sizes:

	Length cm	Breadth cm
A	12	1
B	11	1
C	10	1
D	9	1
E	8	1
F	7	1
G	6	1
H	5	1
I	4	1
J	3	1
K	2	1
L	1	1

Letter the rectangles A, B, C, etc.

On your desk place the rectangles in order of size starting with rectangle A.

(1) How many rectangles like G are needed to make rectangle A? What fraction of A is G?

(2) How many rectangles like J are needed to make rectangle A? What fraction of A is J?

(3) How many rectangles like L are needed to make rectangle A? What fraction of A is L?

(4) How many rectangles like L are needed to make F? What fraction of F is L?

(5) What fraction of G is J?

(6) What fraction of A is K?

(7) How many rectangles like I are needed to make one like A? What fraction of A is I?

(8) What fraction of I is L?

(9) Lay rectangle K on top of A. Which other rectangle is needed to cover A exactly?

(10) Lay rectangle L on top of A. Which other rectangle is needed
to cover A exactly?

(11) Can you write down other pairs of rectangles which will just cover A?

(12) In (9) we found that K and C were needed to cover A exactly. Write this result as K + C = A. Complete the following:

(a) D +   = A   (b) C +   = A

(c)   + I = A   (d)   + F = A.

(13) Which rectangle will H and G cover exactly?

(14) Which rectangle will I and L cover exactly?

(15) Complete the following:

(a) E +   = C   (b) K +   = D

(c) E +   = B   (d)   + L = D

(e) G + J =   (f)   +   = J

(g)   +   = I   (h)   +   = H.

10.7

Using graph paper, draw a square whose sides equal twelve small squares.

Now draw lines across your page on top of the printed lines so that your square is divided into twelve strips.

Number the strips from 1 to 12. Starting from the left-hand side, shade strip 1 in coloured pencil. Now shade half of strip 2, a third of strip 3, a quarter of strip 4, a fifth of strip 5, a sixth of strip six, and so on.

Join the tips of each of the shaded rectangles with a curve.

Have you seen this curve before?

Use your drawing to answer the following.

(1) How many quarters make a half?

(2) How many halves make one?

(3) How many eighths make a quarter?

(4) How many sixths make a half?

(5) What fraction of a half is a quarter?

(6) How many quarters make three-quarters?

(7) What fraction of three-quarters is one-quarter?

(8) What fraction of a half is one-sixth?

10.8

(1) Using graph paper, draw a rectangle twenty-four small squares by one small square.

(a) Shade in pencil half of this rectangle.

(b) Now in ink shade in half of what is left. What fraction of the whole strip is now shaded?

10.9　(c) Now shade in pencil half of what is left. What fraction is shaded now? What fraction is unshaded?

(d) Now shade in ink half of what is left. What fraction is shaded now? What fraction is unshaded?

(2) Draw a second rectangle the same size as the first.

(a) Mark the line dividing the length of the rectangle into halves, similarly mark in the quarter and three-quarters.

(b) Now mark in the eighths. How many eighths are there in a half and in a quarter?

(c) Now divide your rectangle into thirds and mark them.

(3) Draw a third rectangle like the other two.

(a) Shade a fifth of the rectangle.

(b) Starting from the other end of the rectangle shade a fifth of it. What fraction of the rectangle is unshaded?

10.9

Using graph paper, draw four rectangles each twenty-four five millimetre squares by one five-millimetre square.

Divide the first into two equal parts, the second into three equal parts, the third into six equal parts, and the fourth into twelve equal parts.

By looking at your rectangles find the answers to the following:

(1) How many twelfths are needed to make a third?

$$\frac{1}{3} = \frac{}{12}.$$

(2) How many sixths are needed to make a third?

$$\frac{1}{3} = \frac{}{6}.$$

(3) How many twelfths are needed to make a half?

$$\frac{1}{2} = \frac{}{12}.$$

Now working in a similar way fill in the blanks in the following questions:

(4) $\frac{1}{3} = \frac{}{6}$ 　　　(5) $\frac{1}{6} = \frac{}{12}$ 　　　(6) $\frac{1}{2} = \frac{3}{}$

(7) $\frac{5}{6} = \frac{}{12}$ 　　　(8) $\frac{2}{3} = \frac{12}{}$ 　　　(9) $\frac{8}{12} = \frac{}{6} = \frac{}{3} = \frac{12}{}.$

10.10

Can you use the method suggested by the pattern of numbers obtained in 10.9 (9) to fill in the blanks below?

(1) $\dfrac{1}{3} = \dfrac{2}{6} = \dfrac{8}{12} = \dfrac{8}{24} = \dfrac{}{48}$

(2) $\dfrac{1}{4} = \dfrac{}{8} = \dfrac{4}{} = \dfrac{5}{20} = \dfrac{}{40}$

(3) $\dfrac{1}{2} = \dfrac{2}{4} = \dfrac{4}{} = \dfrac{}{16} = \dfrac{16}{}$

(4) $\dfrac{1}{2} = \dfrac{}{2 \times 3} = \dfrac{9}{2 \times 9} = \dfrac{}{2 \times 27}$

(5) $\dfrac{1}{2} = \dfrac{2}{2 \times 2} = \dfrac{4}{} = \dfrac{}{2 \times 8} = \dfrac{16}{} = \dfrac{}{2 \times 24}$

(6) $\dfrac{1}{3} = \dfrac{}{3 \times 3} = \dfrac{9}{}.$

Fractions like those above are called *equivalent fractions*. (4), (5), (6) could be written as a set in this way:

$$A = \left\{ \dfrac{1}{2}, \dfrac{2}{2 \times 2}, \dfrac{3}{2 \times 3}, ----, \dfrac{n}{2 \times n} \right\}$$

$$B = \left\{ \dfrac{1}{3}, \dfrac{2}{3 \times 2}, \dfrac{3}{3 \times 3}, ----, \dfrac{n}{3 \times n} \right\}$$

$$C = \left\{ \dfrac{2}{4}, \dfrac{4}{4 \times 2}, \dfrac{6}{4 \times 3}, ----, \dfrac{2n}{4 \times n} \right\}.$$

The member of the set containing n is called the general term for the sequence of fractions.

10.11
Write down three other members of each of these sets of equivalent fractions and also the general term:

(1) $D = \left\{ \dfrac{2}{3}, \dfrac{4}{3 \times 2}, \dfrac{6}{3 \times 3}, --- \right\}$

(2) $E = \left\{ \dfrac{1}{4}, \dfrac{2}{4 \times 2}, \dfrac{3}{4 \times 3}, --- \right\}$

(3) $F = \left\{ \dfrac{3}{4}, \dfrac{6}{8}, \dfrac{9}{12}, --- \right\}$

(4) $G = \left\{ \dfrac{2}{5}, \dfrac{4}{10}, \dfrac{6}{15}, --- \right\}.$

10.12
What name is given to a set of fractions of the form:
$$A = \{\tfrac{1}{2}, \tfrac{2}{4}, \tfrac{3}{6}, ---\}?$$
The numerators and denominators of these fractions are taken from the set N (natural numbers). Can you put into words the relationship between numerator and denominator for all members of this set?

10.13
Take a sheet of five millimetre graph paper, call one axis N (numerator) and the other D (denominator). Number the axes from 1 to 22 in each case.
Now for fractions from the set $A = \{\tfrac{1}{2}, \tfrac{2}{4}, \tfrac{3}{6}, \tfrac{4}{8}, ---\}$ plot the numerator against the denominator. What do you notice about the set of points you have plotted? Join them up.
From your graph find three other members of this set. What is the nth member or general term of the set? What can you say about points (and the fractions they represent) (a) above the line, and (b) below the line?
Repeat the above work for the set $B = \{\tfrac{1}{3}, \tfrac{2}{6}, \tfrac{3}{9}, ---\}$.

10.14
Draw a rectangle in your graph book six squares by one square and shade in a third of it:

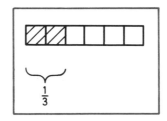

then shade in two-thirds of it starting from the other end:

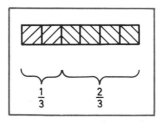

The whole rectangle is now shaded so $\tfrac{1}{3} + \tfrac{2}{3} = \tfrac{3}{3} = 1$.
Use a similar method to add $\tfrac{1}{5}$ and $\tfrac{2}{5}$.

166

(Use a rectangle ten squares by one square.)

Shade first one-fifth and then two-fifths of the rectangle. How many fifths have been shaded? You should find that $\frac{1}{5} + \frac{2}{5} = \frac{3}{5}$.

Work the following in the same way:

(1) $\frac{1}{9} + \frac{4}{9}$ (2) $\frac{3}{7} + \frac{1}{7}$ (3) $\frac{4}{11} + \frac{6}{11}$

(4) $\frac{1}{6} + \frac{7}{6}$ (5) $\frac{1}{9} + \frac{2}{9}$ (6) $\frac{1}{8} + \frac{3}{8}$.

Copy the following and fill in the boxes so that the statements are complete:

(7) $\frac{2}{9} + \frac{7}{9} = \square$ (8) $\frac{3}{7} + \frac{4}{7} = \square$

(9) $\square + \frac{2}{5} = \frac{5}{5}$ (10) $\frac{3}{4} + \square = \frac{4}{4}$

(11) $\square + \frac{1}{11} = \frac{11}{11}$ (12) $\frac{1}{12} + \square = \frac{4}{12}$

(13) $\square + \frac{2}{9} = \frac{7}{9}$ (14) $\frac{1}{6} + \square = \frac{5}{6}$.

What is:

(15) $\frac{2}{7} + \frac{3}{7}$ (16) $\frac{4}{9} + \frac{2}{9}$ (17) $\frac{4}{11} + \frac{5}{11}$?

10.15

Let us now find the value of $\frac{1}{4} + \frac{2}{3}$.

Can we find fractions equivalent to $\frac{1}{4}$ and $\frac{2}{3}$ with the same denominator? Write down some fractions equivalent to $\frac{1}{4}$ and $\frac{2}{3}$:

$$\frac{1}{4} = \frac{2}{8} = \left(\frac{3}{12}\right) = \frac{4}{16} \text{---}$$

and

$$\frac{2}{3} = \frac{4}{6} = \left(\frac{8}{12}\right) = \frac{16}{24} \text{---}$$

Now the ringed fractions have the same denominator so $\frac{1}{4} + \frac{2}{3}$ can be written as $\frac{3}{12} + \frac{8}{12} = \frac{11}{12}$, or in a diagram:

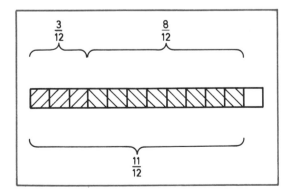

Note that eleven parts of the rectangle are shaded or $\frac{11}{12}$ are shaded.

In a similar way $\frac{3}{7} + \frac{1}{3}$ can be worked

since $\quad \frac{3}{7} = \frac{6}{14} = \left(\frac{9}{21}\right) = \frac{12}{28}$

and $\quad \frac{1}{3} = \frac{2}{6} = \frac{3}{9} = \frac{4}{12} = \frac{5}{15} = \frac{6}{18} = \left(\frac{7}{21}\right)$.

10.16 $\frac{3}{7} + \frac{1}{3}$ can be written as $\frac{9}{21} + \left(\frac{7}{21}\right) = \frac{16}{21}$, or in a diagram:

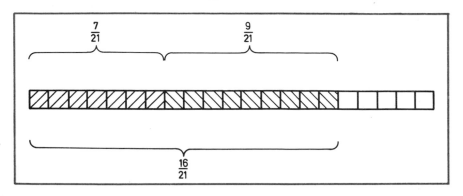

Note that sixteen parts of the rectangle are shaded or $\frac{16}{21}$ are shaded.
Subtraction can be worked in a similar way.
Find the value of $\frac{2}{3} - \frac{1}{5}$.

$$\frac{2}{3} = \frac{4}{6} = \frac{6}{9} = \frac{8}{12} = \left(\frac{10}{15}\right) = \frac{12}{18}$$

and

$$\frac{1}{5} = \frac{2}{10} = \left(\frac{3}{15}\right) = \frac{4}{20}.$$

So $\frac{2}{3} - \frac{1}{5}$ can be written as $\frac{10}{15} - \frac{3}{15} = \frac{7}{15}$, or in a diagram:

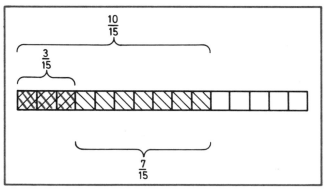

The black shading represents $\frac{10}{15}$ and the blue shading $\frac{3}{15}$.
The area left with black shading when the blue is removed is $\frac{7}{15}$.
Discuss with your teacher the method used in each of these
examples.

10.16

Now try these in the same way:

(1) $\frac{1}{4} + \frac{1}{5}$ (2) $\frac{3}{4} + \frac{2}{3}$ (3) $\frac{2}{5} + \frac{1}{3}$

(4) $\frac{4}{5} + \frac{1}{2}$ (5) $\frac{3}{4} + \frac{1}{2}$ (6) $\frac{1}{4} + \frac{4}{5}$

(7) $\frac{1}{9} + \frac{1}{3}$ (8) $\frac{3}{5} + \frac{3}{4}$ (9) $\frac{3}{7} + \frac{3}{4}$

(10) $\frac{2}{9} + \frac{4}{5}$ (11) $\frac{6}{7} - \frac{4}{5}$ (12) $\frac{1}{8} + \frac{1}{4} + \frac{1}{2}$

(13) $\frac{3}{8} + \frac{3}{4} + \frac{5}{16}$ (14) $\frac{2}{3} + \frac{4}{9}$ (15) $\frac{4}{5} - \frac{3}{7}$

(16) $\frac{8}{9} - \frac{1}{7}$ (17) $\frac{6}{7} - \frac{1}{3}$ (18) $\frac{4}{11} - \frac{1}{9}.$

10.17

We have found a way of adding two numbers in our new set of fractions, but can we add $3 + \frac{1}{4}$?

3 belongs to which set?

3 belongs to the set N and $\frac{1}{4}$ belongs to the set of fractions. Can we add members of different sets? We have not yet found a method. Can we find a number equivalent to $\frac{1}{4}$ in set N? No.

Can we find a number equivalent to 3 in the set of fractions? We found earlier that there are four quarters in a whole, so in 3 there must be twelve quarters, thus $3 \in N$ is equivalent to $\frac{12}{4} \in F$. (We use F to stand for the set of fractions.)

Complete the following:

(1) $3 \in N$ is equivalent to $\frac{}{1} \in F$.

(2) $4 \in N$ is equivalent to $\frac{}{1} \in F$.

(3) $2 \in N$ is equivalent to $\frac{}{2} \in F$.

(4) $4 \in N$ is equivalent to $\frac{}{4} \in F$.

(5) $6 \in N$ is equivalent to $\frac{}{2} \in F$.

So to add 3 and $\frac{1}{4}$ we find a number in F equivalent to 3, i.e., 3 is equivalent to $\frac{12}{4}$. Then $3 + \frac{1}{4} = \frac{12}{4} + \frac{1}{4} = \frac{13}{4} = 3\frac{1}{4}$.

Similarly $4 + \frac{1}{3}$ is the same as $\frac{12}{3} + \frac{1}{3} = \frac{13}{3} = 4\frac{1}{3}$.

10.18

Now work these in the same way:

(1) $4 + \frac{1}{4}$ (2) $3 + \frac{1}{5}$ (3) $2 + \frac{4}{5}$

(4) $3 + \frac{5}{7}$ (5) $\frac{3}{8} + 5$ (6) $1 + \frac{1}{7}$

(7) $1 + \frac{3}{4}$ (8) $2 + \frac{3}{5}$ (9) $1 + \frac{9}{10}$.

10.19

$3\frac{1}{4}$ is a mixed number since it contains whole numbers (members of N) and fractions (members of F).

$\frac{3}{4}$ is a proper fraction.

$\frac{7}{3}$ is an improper fraction. Can you suggest why?

10.20

(1) What is $\frac{4}{3}$ as a mixed number?

$$\frac{4}{3} = \frac{3}{3} + \frac{1}{3} = 1 + \frac{1}{3} \text{ or } 1\frac{1}{3}.$$

(2) What is $\frac{7}{2}$ as a mixed number?

$$\frac{7}{2} = \frac{6}{2} + \frac{1}{2} = 3 + \frac{1}{2} = 3\frac{1}{2}.$$

Can you suggest what the following are as mixed numbers?

(3) $\frac{5}{3}$ (4) $\frac{5}{2}$ (5) $\frac{9}{5}$

(6) $\frac{11}{3}$ (7) $\frac{16}{7}$ (8) $\frac{14}{4}$.

Change the following to improper fractions:

(9) $2\frac{1}{6}$ (10) $1\frac{1}{4}$ (11) $2\frac{1}{2}$

(12) $5\frac{1}{3}$ (13) $3\frac{2}{3}$ (14) $2\frac{3}{8}$

(15) $3\frac{4}{9}$ (16) $4\frac{3}{7}$ (17) $2\frac{4}{5}$.

10.21

Can you suggest how we could add or subtract two fractions like $2\frac{1}{4}$ and $1\frac{1}{5}$?

First change them to improper fractions:

$$2\frac{1}{4} = \frac{9}{4} \qquad 1\frac{1}{5} = \frac{6}{5}.$$

Then add: $\frac{9}{4} + \frac{6}{5} = \frac{45}{20} + \frac{24}{20} = \frac{69}{20} = 3\frac{9}{20}.$

Similarly: $3\frac{4}{9} - 2\frac{1}{7} = \frac{31}{9} - \frac{15}{7}$

$$= \frac{217}{63} - \frac{135}{63}$$

$$= \frac{82}{63} = 1\frac{19}{63}.$$

Now try these:

(1) $1\frac{1}{5} + 2\frac{1}{3}$ (2) $1\frac{7}{9} + \frac{1}{2}$ (3) $2\frac{3}{5} + 1\frac{1}{4}$

(4) $3\frac{1}{7} - 1\frac{1}{2}$ (5) $4\frac{6}{11} - 2\frac{1}{2}$ (6) $1\frac{2}{3} + 4\frac{1}{7}$

(7) $4\frac{4}{9} - 2\frac{1}{3}$ (8) $1\frac{6}{7} + 2\frac{1}{3} - \frac{2}{3}$ (9) $1\frac{4}{7} + 2\frac{1}{5} - 1\frac{4}{5}$

(10) $1\frac{1}{3} + 2\frac{1}{4} - 1\frac{1}{6}$ (11) $4\frac{1}{5} + 2\frac{1}{6}$ (12) $3\frac{1}{4} + 2\frac{4}{5} - 1\frac{1}{5}$

(13) $3\frac{2}{3} + 2\frac{6}{7} - 1\frac{1}{2}$ (14) $3\frac{5}{6} + 1\frac{1}{2} - 4\frac{1}{3}$ (15) $7\frac{1}{4} - 3\frac{3}{5}$

(16) $5\frac{1}{2} + 2\frac{5}{6} - 3\frac{1}{3}$ (17) $1\frac{4}{5} + 2\frac{1}{3} - 3\frac{1}{2}$ (18) $\frac{6}{5} + 1 - \frac{4}{3}$.

Interest page

A revision game

Two members of the class write down an equation of a straight line.
The rest of the class then have to find what this equation is. Values
of x are given to the authors of the equation who substitute these
values of x and calculate the corresponding values of y. The resulting ordered pairs are written on the blackboard. When five ordered
pairs have been placed on the board, the rest of the class must give
the equation of the line. If they fail to give the correct equation, then
the two authors score one point and set another equation for the
class to find. This procedure is repeated until a correct equation is
given. Then two other members of the class make up a new equation.
The winning pair are the pupils who have the highest number of
points.

This game could also be organized in the form of a team quiz, with
half of the class against the other half.

11. Turning in circles

The village of Angleford

11.1

The position of the church on the grid can be found by using the ordered pair (2, 3). Write down the ordered pairs for the following places on the map using the same order as for the church.

(1) The cross-roads   (2) Angleford station
(3) Wheeler's Mill   (4) Angleford Manor

From Angleford church tower one has a clear view of the whole village. Imagine that you are standing on the tower of the church and answer the following:
(1) If you start facing the mill and turn through a complete turn where are you now facing?
(2) If you start facing the cross-roads and turn through a complete turn, where are you now facing?
(3) If you start facing the station and turn through a complete turn, where are you facing?

11.3
In the following, state the direction in which you are facing after completing your turn.
(1) You start facing the mill and turn through half a complete turn to the left.
(2) You start facing the mill and turn through half a complete turn to the right.
(3) You start facing the manor and turn left through half a complete turn.
(4) You start facing the manor and turn right through half a complete turn.
(5) You start facing the cross-roads and turn left through half a complete turn.
(6) You start facing the station and turn left through a quarter of a complete turn.
(7) You start facing the manor and turn left through a quarter of a complete turn.
(8) You start facing the manor and turn right through a quarter of a complete turn.
(9) You start facing the cross-roads and turn left through three-quarters of a complete turn.
(10) You start facing the mill and turn right through three-quarters of a complete turn.

11.4
(1) If you stand at the mill facing the church and turn through one complete turn, in what direction will you now be facing?
(2) If you stand at the cross-roads facing Brown's farm and turn through three complete turns what direction are you now facing?
(3) If you stand at Wheeler's Mill facing the church and turn through two complete turns to the left, in what direction are you facing on completing your turn?
(4) If you stand at Wheeler's Mill facing the school and turn

through two complete turns to the right, in what direction are you facing on completing your turn?

(5) If you stand at the church facing the manor and turn through one and a half turns to the right, what direction are you facing on completing your turn?

(6) If you stand at the church facing the manor and turn through one and a half complete turns to the left, what direction are you facing on completing your turn?

11.5

In the previous examples we have been dealing with different amounts of turn. An amount of turn is called an *angle*.
So far the angles used have been fairly easy to measure, because we have confined ourselves to halves, quarters, and complete turns.
Suppose that you were standing at the church facing Wheeler's Mill and you turned to the right to face the ford. What fraction of a complete turn would you have turned through?
This question is difficult because before we can find the value of this angle we need some way of measuring it.

11.6

If the scale of the map of Angleford is one unit to one kilometre, write down (a) the distance on the map between the following places in units, and (b) the actual distance between these places in kilometres.
(1) The church and the manor.
(2) The church and Wheeler's Mill.
(3) Wheeler's Mill and the cross-roads.
(4) The station and the manor.
(5) The cross-roads and the church.

11.7

To make a simple angle measure or protractor, using a square piece of tracing paper ten centimetres by ten centimetres, fold the paper in half and in half again. Open out the paper.
If the folds do not show up very well, make them clearer with a sharp pencil – do not make your lines too thick.

11.8

In order to measure anything we have to decide on our units of measure. Some examples of units of measure are:
(1) for length: centimetres, metres, and kilometres.

(2) for area: square centimetres, square metres, etc.
Write down four more examples of units of measure.
We are going to use as our unit of measure for angles, one complete turn. In our simple protractor we have split the complete turn
up into four parts. Each of these quarters of a complete turn is
called a *right angle*.

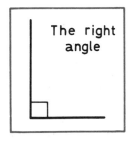

The square is used to show that the angle drawn is a right angle.

11.9

(1) Look at the following angles, they all have something in common. Can you describe them?

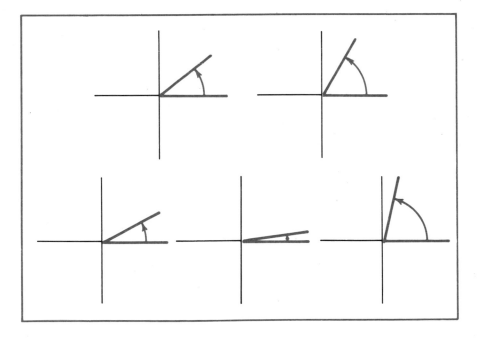

Angles of this type are called *acute angles*.
Look up acute in your dictionary.
(2) Why are angles of this type called acute?
Which of the following angles are acute?

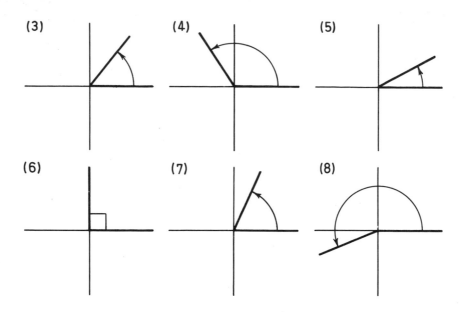

The next largest angle is the right angle, which we have already met. Look at the following angles and say which are right angles:

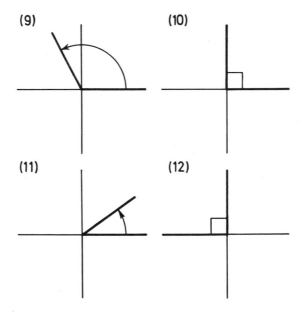

Look around your classroom and see if you can find any examples of right angles. Make a note of these. Use your protractor to measure the angles formed by the corners of this book, are they right angles?

(13) Look at the following types of angle. Again they all have something in common. Can you say what it is?

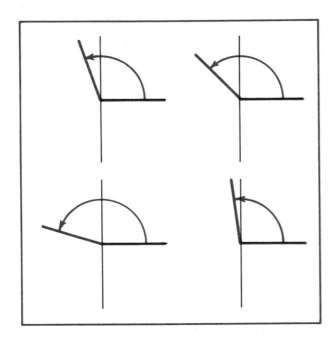

Angles of this type are called *obtuse angles.*
Look up obtuse in your dictionary.
Look at the following angles. Which of them are obtuse angles?

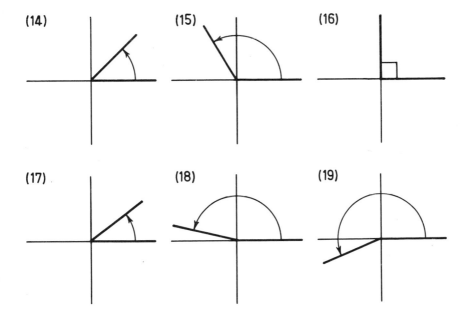

If we fit two right angles together we have a straight line (i.e., $\frac{1}{4}$
turn + $\frac{1}{4}$ turn = $\frac{1}{2}$ turn).

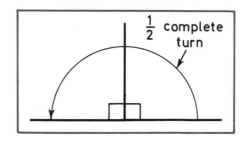

Look at the following angles and say which of them form straight lines:

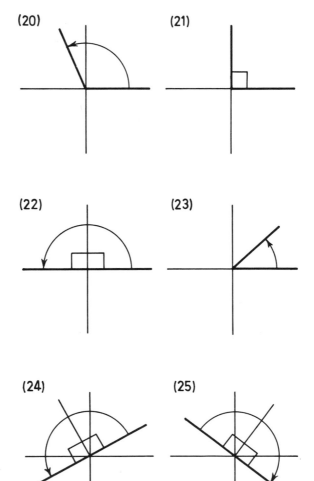

(26) Look at the following angles. Can you say what they have in common?

178

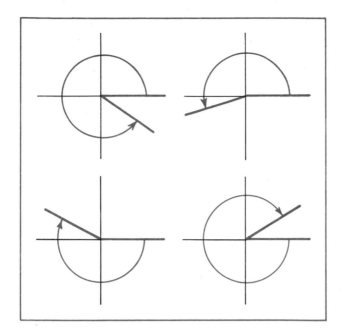

Angles of this type are called *reflex angles*.
Look up reflex in your dictionary.
Look at the following angles and say whether they are acute, obtuse, right, or reflex angles or straight lines.

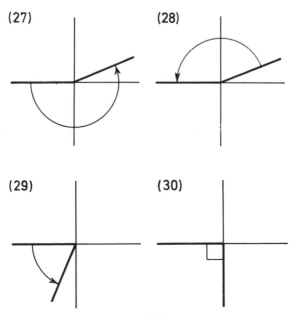

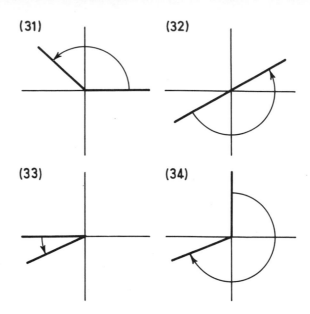

(31) (32) (33) (34)

11.10

Copy the following statements and fill in the blanks with the terms 'greater than', 'less than', or 'equal to', as appropriate.

(1) An acute angle is _____ no turn and _____ a quarter of a complete turn.

(2) A right angle is _____ a quarter of a complete turn.

(3) An obtuse angle is _____ a quarter of a complete turn and _____ half a complete turn.

(4) A reflex angle is ———— half a complete turn and ———— 360°.

(5) Using the symbols >, <, and = as appropriate and writing 't' to stand for one complete turn, shorten the above statements.

11.11

Use your protractor to measure the following angles and state the type of angle in each case:

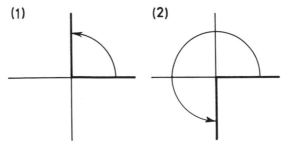

(1) (2)

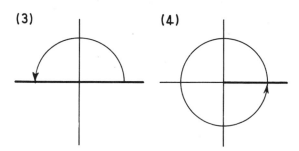

(3) (4)

State the amount of turn in the following angles:

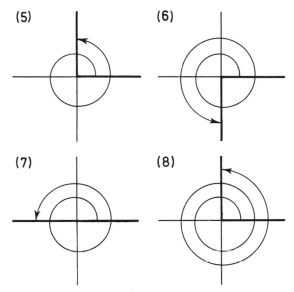

(5) (6)

(7) (8)

11.12

(1) Use your protractor to draw a right angle.

Write down the number of right angles in the following:

(2) a complete turn   (3) half a complete turn

(4) a quarter of a complete turn

(5) three-quarters of a complete turn

(6) two complete turns   (7) no turn

(8) three and a half complete turns

(9) four complete turns   (10) nine complete turns.

11.13

Look at the following acute angle:

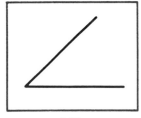

181

11.14　(1) Can this angle be measured with your protractor?
(2) Estimate the size of this angle in terms of a complete turn.
(3) Estimate the size of the angle in terms of a right angle.
If we wish to measure acute angles like this one with our protractor, we will have to make the protractor more accurate by increasing the number of folds. Take your protractor and fold it along the diagonals as shown:

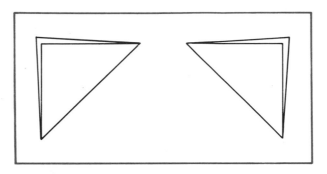

Open out the paper. It should now look like this:

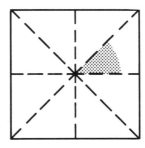

(4) What fraction of a complete turn is the shaded angle?
(5) Write down the set of angles that we can now measure with our protractor (a) in terms of complete turns, and (b) in terms of right angles.
(6) Use your protractor to measure the acute angle in (1) and write down your answer. Did you estimate this angle correctly?

11.14
Use your protractor to measure the following angles. Give your answers (a) in fractions of complete turns, and (b) in right angles.

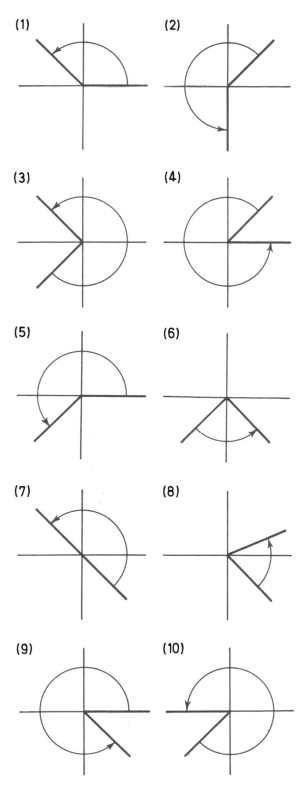

11.15

Use your protractor to construct the following angles:
(1) $\frac{7}{8}$ of a complete turn   (2) $1\frac{1}{2}$ right angles
(3) $\frac{3}{8}$ of a complete turn   (4) $3\frac{1}{2}$ right angles
(5) $\frac{2}{8}$ of a complete turn   (6) $2\frac{1}{2}$ complete turns
(7) $\frac{1}{2}$ of a right angle   (8) $\frac{1}{8}$ of a complete turn
(9) $4\frac{1}{2}$ right angles   (10) $\frac{9}{8}$ of a complete turn.

For numbers (1) to (5) state whether the angle you have drawn is acute, obtuse, reflex, or a right angle.

We could go on increasing the accuracy of our protractor by dividing our complete turn up into sixteenths of a complete turn, then thirty-seconds of a complete turn, and so on.

It is thought that the Babylonians were the first to divide up a complete turn into three hundred and sixty parts and this idea was later followed up by the Greeks who called one-three-hundred-and-sixtieth ($\frac{1}{360}$) of a complete turn *one degree*. One degree is written as $1°$. This is the system that we use today. In this system one complete turn is written as $360°$ (three hundred and sixty degrees). Half a complete turn is then $180°$ (one hundred and eighty degrees) and a quarter of a complete turn is $90°$.

11.16

Change the units of the following angles to degrees:
  (1) 1 complete turn   (2) $\frac{1}{2}$ of a complete turn
  (3) $\frac{1}{360}$ of a complete turn   (4) $\frac{1}{4}$ of a complete turn
  (5) $\frac{3}{4}$ of a complete turn   (6) 1 right angle
  (7) 2 right angles   (8) $\frac{1}{8}$ of a complete turn
  (9) $\frac{1}{2}$ of a right angle   (10) $\frac{3}{8}$ of a complete turn
(11) $\frac{1}{6}$ of a complete turn   (12) $\frac{1}{3}$ of a right angle.

In each of the above examples name the type of angle.
Copy the following and fill in the spaces:
(13) _____° < an acute angle < _____°
(14) A right angle = _____°
(15) _____° < an obtuse angle < _____°
(16) —° < a reflex angle < —°.

11.17

The Greek letters α (alpha) and θ (theta) are often used to stand for angles. Find the number of degrees in the angles α and θ in the following diagrams. Do not use a protractor.

(1)   **(2)**

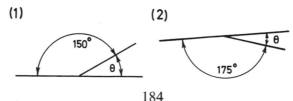

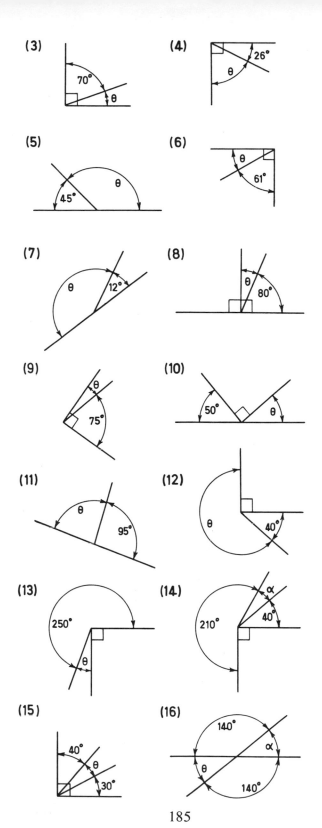

(3) 70° θ

(4) 26° θ

(5) 45° θ

(6) θ 61°

(7) θ 12°

(8) θ 80°

(9) θ 75°

(10) 50° θ

(11) θ 95°

(12) θ 40°

(13) 250° θ

(14) α 40° 210°

(15) 40° θ 30°

(16) 140° α θ 140°

7

11.18   When the sum of a number of angles is 90°, the angles are said to be *complementary*.

When the sum of a number of angles is 180°, the angles are said to be *supplementary*.

Thus in (3) the angles 70° and 20° are complementary, i.e., 70° + 20° = 90°, and in (1) the angles 150° and 30° are supplementary, i.e., 150° + 30° = 180°.

11.18

In the following examples state whether the angles given are complementary, supplementary, or neither.

(1) 70°, 20°   (2) 10°, 8°, 72°
(3) 15°, 35°, 130°   (4) 5°, 65°, 20°
(5) 55°, 15°   (6) 13°, 23°, 33°, 43°, 53°, 25°
(7) 165°, 35°   (8) 2°, 12°, 22°, 32°, 22°
(9) 125°, 10°, 5°, 25°, 15°   (10) 0°, 90°, 70°, 20°.

What can you say about the angles α and θ in the following statements?

(11) $\alpha + \theta = 180°$ (12) $0 < \alpha < 90°$
(13) $90° < \theta < 180°$ (14) $180° < \alpha < 360°$.

11.19

In order to answer the following problems you will need a more accurate protractor.

When using this protractor to measure an angle, the base line of the protractor is placed along one of the lines of the angle, with the centre of the protractor on the point of the angle:

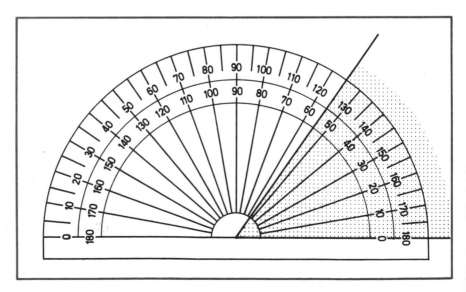

The reading is taken from the inner scale of the protractor, and in this case the angle measured is 55°. Make quite sure that whenever you measure an angle you measure it from 0. Look at the following diagram:

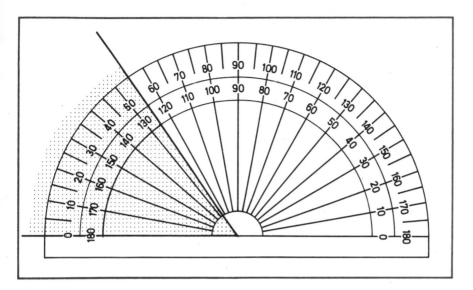

In this case we are measuring the acute angle shown and here we have to use the outer scale of the protractor. Again the angle is 55°. It is a good idea to estimate the size of the angle before measuring it.

11.20

Estimate the size of each of the following angles:

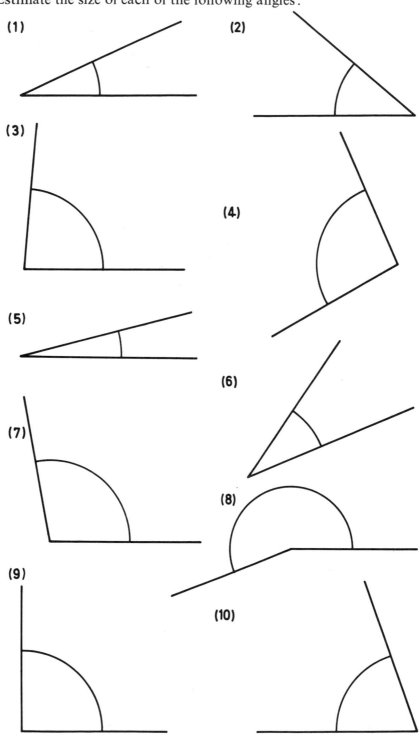

(1)

(2)

(3)

(4)

(5)

(6)

(7)

(8)

(9)

(10)

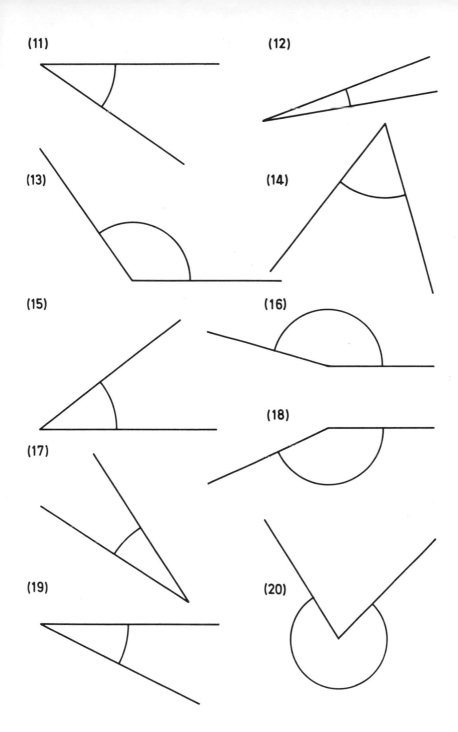

Now measure each of the angles using your protractor.
Use your protractor to construct the following angles:
(21) 12°   (22) 180°
(23) 73°   (24) 158°

(25) 106°   (26) 69°
(27) 232°   (28) 84°
(29) 114°   (30) 305°.

11.21

(1) Draw a line AC of length 8 *cm*

A _____ C

8*cm*.

(2) Put the centre point of your protractor on A with the base line along AC and construct an angle of 30°.

(3) Put the centre point of your protractor on C with the base line along AC and construct an angle of 20°.

(4) Label the point where the lines cross, B.

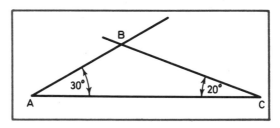

11.22

Use your protractor and ruler to construct the following triangles using AC for the base line:

(1) AC = 5 *cm*, angle A = 35°, and angle C = 25°
(2) AC = 9 *cm*, angle A = 45°, and angle C = 30°
(3) AC = 10 *cm*, angle A = 24°, and angle C = 90°
(4) AC = 8 *cm*, angle A = 10°, and angle C = 110°
(5) AC = 6 *cm*, angle A = 30°, and angle C = 30°
(6) AC = 8 *cm*, angle A = 60°, and angle C = 60°.

(7) Measure angle B in each of the triangles you have constructed and copy and complete the following table:

	(1)	(2)	(3)	(4)	(5)	(6)
angle A	35°	45°	24°	10°	30°	60°
angle C	25°	30°	90°	110°	30°	60°
angle B						
sum of the angles						

190

(8) What conclusion can you draw from this table? Make a note of this important result, i.e., the angles of a triangle add up to ____°.

(9) Look at the triangles you have constructed in (5) and (6). These triangles are a little different from the others because they have special properties. Triangle (5) is an *isosceles triangle* and triangle (6) is an *equilateral triangle*. You met both these types of triangle in chapter 3. Write down all the properties that you can find for each triangle. Why is triangle (5) not an equilateral triangle?

(10) We could show that the angles of a triangle are supplementary by a different method. Using your protractor and ruler construct a triangle of any dimensions you wish. Cut the triangle out and tear off each of the angles. Try to fit the angles together so that their sum is clearly 180°.

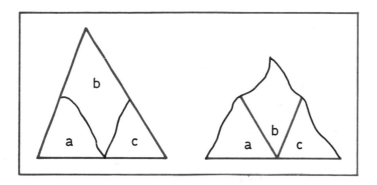

11.23

The angles of a triangle are supplementary, i.e., when added together they make 180°.

Use this fact to find the unmarked angles in the following diagrams:

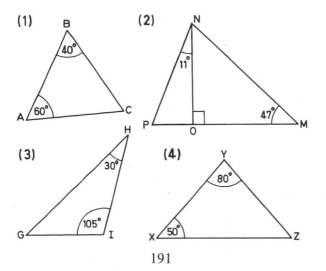

191

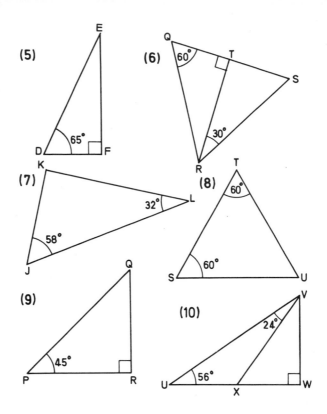

From the triangles above list the following sets of triangles. Use △ as shorthand for triangle, for example, △ABC reads 'triangle ABC'.

(11) The set of right-angled triangles. There are nine elements in this set. Call this set P.

(12) The set of isosceles triangles. There are four elements in this set. Call this set Q.

(13) The set of equilateral triangles. There are two elements in this set. Call this set R.

(14) From the above sets write down the following new sets:

(a) P ∩ Q   (b) P ∩ R   (c) Q ∩ R.

(15) Can you explain why the answer to (14)(b) will always be an empty set?

11.24

For the following work you will need a pair of compasses.

(1) Use your protractor to construct an angle of 120° with AO = OC = 4 *cm*. Draw the lines AO and OC with a sharp pencil, as in the diagram on the opposite page.

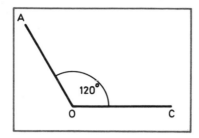

Now put your compass point on O and with the radius equal to
4 *cm* draw a circle with O as the centre.

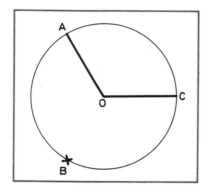

Change the radius of your compasses to the length AC and step off
the length AC around the circumference of the circle. You should
now have three points on the circumference of your circle A, C, and
another point, call this point B. Join up the points A, B, and C.
This is the equilateral triangle.

(2) What can you say about the three obtuse angles at O? They all
have something in common.

(3) In order to construct the equilateral triangle we started by
drawing an angle of 120°. Can you say why we chose this angle? It
has something to do with the number of sides and the complete
turn of 360°.

(4) What can you say about the areas of the three sectors of the circle?

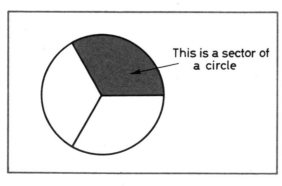

This is a sector of
a circle

7*

11.25

(1) Use your protractor to construct a right angle AOB with AO = OB = 4 *cm*. Again draw the lines AO and OB very faintly.

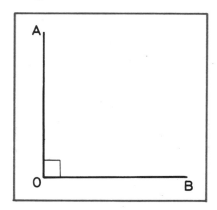

(2) With the radius of your compasses equal to 4 *cm*, draw a circle with centre O.

(3) Now change the radius of your compasses to the length AB and step off this length around the circumference of your circle. This should give you two new points. Label these points C and D.

(4) Join up the points A to B, B to C, C to D, and D to A. The figure we now have is the square; you have met it before.

(5) What can you say about the four angles at the centre of the circle?

(6) In order to construct this square, we started by drawing an angle of 90°. Can you say why we chose this angle? Again, it has some connection with the number of sides and the complete turn.

11.26

(1) A polygon is a closed two-dimensional figure constructed with straight lines. Here are some examples:

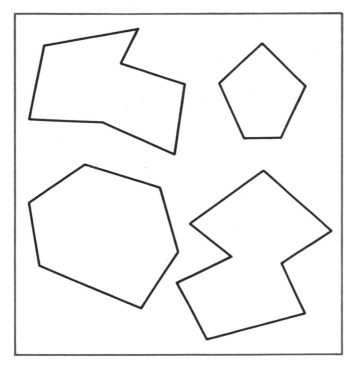

(2) A regular polygon is a polygon with all the sides and all the angles equal.

11.27
Use the methods described in 11.24 and 11.25 to construct further examples of regular polygons. Here are the names of some of them:
a five-sided regular polygon is called a *pentagon*
a six-sided regular polygon is called a *hexagon*
a seven-sided regular polygon is called a *heptagon*
an eight-sided regular polygon is called an *octagon*
a nine-sided regular polygon is called an *ennagon* or *nonagon*
a ten-sided regular polygon is called a *decagon*
an eleven-sided regular polygon is called a *hendecagon* or *unodecagon*
a twelve-sided regular polygon is called a *duodecagon*.
These regular polygons would make an excellent wall chart. They could be cut out of card or coloured paper and stuck on the chart with their description and properties written beside them.
As the number of sides of the polygon increase, compare the shape of the polygon with the circle in which it is placed. The sides of a hundred-sided regular polygon would be very close to the circle and the sides of a thousand-sided regular polygon would be even closer. The largest polygon ever constructed has 65,537 sides and took ten years to construct.

11.27 Copy the following table and complete it for the regular polygons named earlier.

Name	Number of sides	Angle at centre

Interest page

A crossnumber

1	2			3	4
			5		
6				7	
8			9		10
		11			
	12				

Across

1. Area of a square of side 11 *cm*.
3. Area of a rectangle 8 *cm* × 3 *cm*.
5. Ten times the area of a rectangle 7 *cm* square.
6. 18 × 18.
7. Lonesome.
8. Area of rectangle is 42 *cm²*, breadth is 2 *cm*. Length?
9. A perfect number.
11. 8 × 12 − 8 × 4.
12. The sum of the digits is twelve.

Down

2. The sum of the digits is nine.
3. Ten times the tenth prime number plus one.
4. Area of rectangle is 120 *cm²*, breadth is 3 *cm*. Length?
6. The factors of a perfect number.
9. This shaded area:

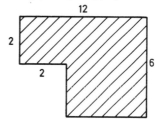

10. Half this area, the lengths are in centimetres.

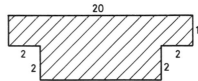

11. The perimeter of this shape, the lengths are in centimetres.

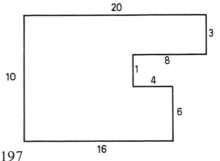

12. Let's find out about statistics

12.1

Someone is always trying to prove something to us by using figures.
(1) A friend tries to prove that he is clever because he has nine
out of ten for his homework whereas other members of the class
only get seven out of ten or less.
(2) Someone else tries to prove that he works harder than anyone
else because he gets £1 for his paper round whereas the normal rate
of pay is only 75*p*.
(3) One town claims to be the best seaside resort because it has an
average of nine hours' sunshine per day during the summer months.
Another claims to be the best because it has more visitors than any
other resort.
(4) A soap manufacturer claims that eight out of ten film stars use
his product.
Comment on these statements.

12.2

The study of statements of this sort and the figures on which they
are based is one aspect of statistics. In this chapter we shall look at
some ways of representing figures in picture form. In later books in
this series you will have opportunities to learn of other methods of
representing numbers and of other branches of statistics.

12.3

If we look back in history, thousands of years to the time when man
first started to keep flocks of sheep and herds of cows, we find the
first use of statistics and the recording of numbers.
In this early period of history man had not yet learned to count as
we know counting today, so he had to find some means of recording
the number of sheep or cows that he owned.
Can you imagine him each evening as he got back to his sheepfold
putting a stone from one bag to another as each sheep went through
the door of the fold? If he had a stone left in his bag he knew that
he had lost one of his sheep.
Some shepherds preferred to use what we call a tally stick; on this

stick a shepherd cut a notch for each of his sheep. As each sheep passed him, he moved his finger along the stick one notch.

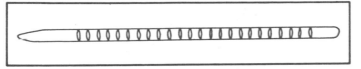

A tally stick

Yet other shepherds used a knotted rope as a tally; there was one knot on the rope for each sheep they owned.

Other shepherds cut a new tally stick each night, then by comparing sticks they could tell whether any sheep had been lost.

One shepherd cut the following sticks during one week.

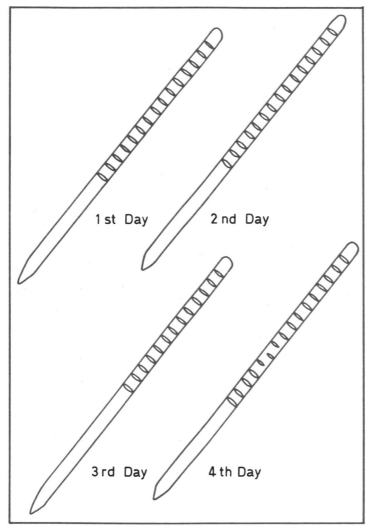

What do the sticks tell the shepherd?

12.4

This method of representing things by a notch or line is often used today to represent information.
Look at the following:

>on Monday four pupils were absent from a form
>on Tuesday three were absent
>on Wednesday none were absent
>on Thursday five were absent
>on Friday two were absent.

We could represent this information in the same sort of way as the shepherd recorded his sheep:

Monday	/ / / /
Tuesday	/ / /
Wednesday	
Thursday	/ / / / /
Friday	/ /

A more attractive way of representing this information is to draw pictures of the pupils:

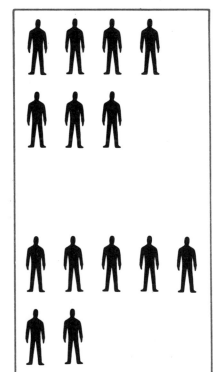

Monday

Tuesday

Wednesday

Thursday

Friday

The school canteen uses the following amounts of potatoes:

January	five sacks
February	four sacks
March	six sacks

Represent this information in a picture diagram as we did above (use a drawing of a sack). Why do you think less potatoes were used in February than in the other two months?

12.6

A dairy farmer sold the following amounts of milk:

1st week	seven churns
2nd week	five churns
3rd week	six churns
4th week	four churns

Represent this information in the form of a picture diagram. What do you think will be the best drawing to use?

12.7

Picture diagrams of this sort are called *pictograms*. If you look in your daily newspaper or comics you will often see pictograms being used to display information.

12.8

Use pictograms to represent the following information:
(1) A housewife went to the butcher's three times in one week: on Monday she spent 35*p*, on Wednesday she spent 45*p*, and on Saturday she spent 60*p*.
(2) A family bought bread as follows: Monday two loaves, Tuesday one loaf, Wednesday four loaves, Friday two loaves, and Saturday six loaves.
(3) A builder completed four houses in March, six in June, and fifteen in November.

12.9

Let us return to the early shepherd recording his sheep. As time progressed his flock grew larger and he needed more and more notches on his stick, until at last his tally stick became too long to manage.
What could he do? Can you suggest what he could do to keep his tally stick to a reasonable length?

12.10

The following tally stick represents one hundred sheep. What has the shepherd done to make this possible?

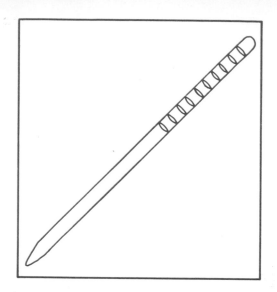

This idea of using one notch to represent a number of sheep is also widely used today. Look at the following:

(1)

This diagram represents two hundred packets of detergent sold by a supermarket. How many packets does each box represent?

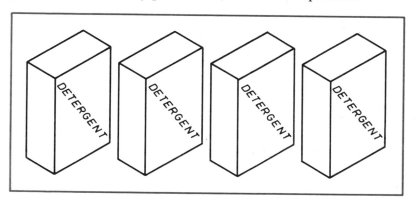

(2) Number of loaves sold by a bread roundsman

Monday

Tuesday

Wednesday

Friday

Saturday

On Monday the roundsman sold 140 loaves. How many did he sell on the other days of the week?

12.11

(1) At a certain school there are 250 girls and 200 boys. How could this information be represented? One way would be to draw a little girl to represent each girl and a boy to represent each boy. Would you like to do this? Keep in mind the suggestion in 12.10 and find a simpler way of representing this information. We could draw one picture of a girl to represent fifty girls in the school and one picture of a boy to represent fifty boys. The information could then be represented in a picture:

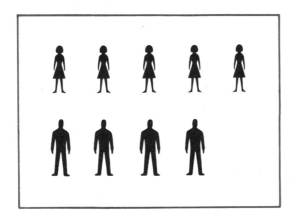

At the school there are also twenty-five teachers. How could the teachers be represented using the same scale? If there were fifty teachers we could draw a whole teacher. As there are only twenty-five, what will we draw?

12.11   We could draw half a person:

(2) In a certain week at the school the following bottles of milk were drunk by the children.

Monday	400
Tuesday	350
Wednesday	425
Thursday	400
Friday	375

Using a drawing of a bottle of milk to stand for fifty bottles, represent this information in a pictogram.

(3) In the following pictogram, one drawing of an ice-cream represents 20 ices sold. How many ices were sold each day?

Number of ices sold

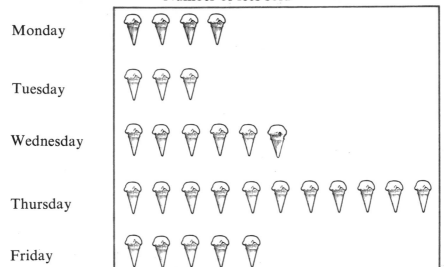

Monday

Tuesday

Wednesday

Thursday

Friday

What can you tell about the weather on Thursday? Can you suggest why sales were low on Tuesday?

(4) In the pictogram below, one drawing of an animal represents 10 animals. How many cows, sheep, and chickens does the farmer own?

Animals   Number of animals a farmer owns

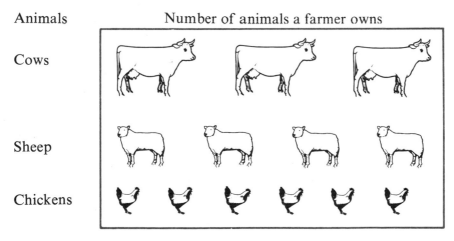

Cows

Sheep

Chickens

(5) Represent the following information in a pictogram. In one week a school kitchen used 1 *tonne* of potatoes, 250 *kg* of peas, 250 *kg* of carrots, and 50 *kg* of meat. (Choose your own pictures, but use the same scale for each item.)

(6) A builder completes fifteen houses in August, eighteen in November, three in February, and six in May. Represent this information in a pictogram. Can you make any comment on these figures?

12.11

(7) A young machine operator in a factory makes twenty items on his first day, thirty on the second, fifty on the third, and then seventy per day, for the rest of the week. Represent these figures on a pictogram. Can you comment on the figures? How long does it take him to learn to use the machine?

(8) The pictogram below was plotted from the results of interviews with a number of housewives in a particular part of the country.

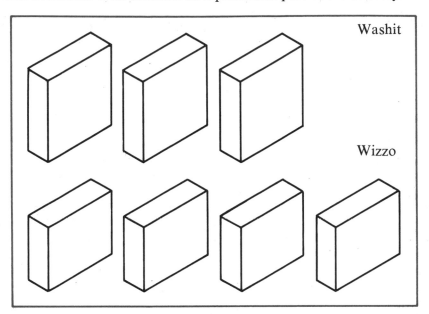

If each packet represents the answers of ten housewives:
(a) how many like Washit?
(b) how many like Wizzo?
(c) which is the more popular brand?
(d) how many housewives were interviewed?
(e) would this necessarily apply to other parts of the country?

(9) A certain number of people were asked how they travelled to work. A pictogram (opposite page) was plotted of the results. Study it, then answer the questions.
If each drawing represents the answers given by ten people:
(a) how many people used each method of transport?
(b) how many people were interviewed?

(10) A cheese manufacturer packs his product in three ways. Twenty-five kilogramme rolls, ten kilogramme blocks, and half kilogramme packets. In one week he sells fifty rolls, one hundred blocks, and two hundred and sixty packets. Represent this information in a pictogram.
(a) How many kilogrammes of cheese does he sell in this week?

(b) If the cheese sells at 35*p* per kilogramme, how much money does he receive?

(c) Do the figures suggest how housewives prefer to buy their cheese?

(11) Draw a pictogram to represent the number of pupils who were absent from your form on each day of last week.

(12) Find out how many cars, lorries, vans, cycles, and motor cycles pass your school gate in one hour. Represent these figures in a pictogram.

(13) Find out how many pupils in your form wear spectacles, have bicycles, have wrist watches. Represent these figures in a pictogram.

(14) Find out how many members of your form come to school by car, by bus, by bicycle, by train, or on foot. Represent these figures in a pictogram.

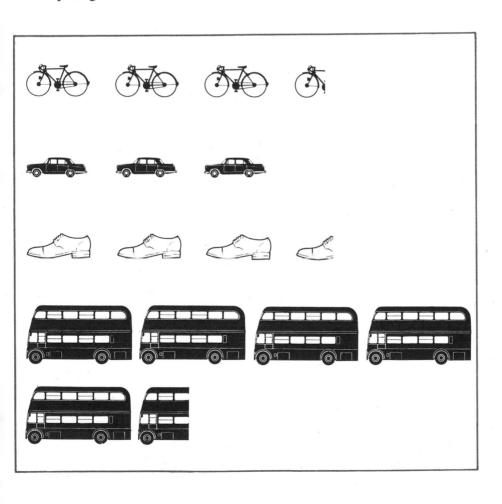

13. Checking up

13.1

In chapter 1 you learnt the following:

A set is a collection of objects, usually with some common feature.
We use curly brackets { } to stand for 'the set of'.
A capital letter can be used to represent a set, for example,
A = {even numbers}.
A subset is usually part of a larger set, for example, {1, 2, 3} is a subset of {1, 2, 3, 4, 5}.
A set may be a subset of itself, for example {1, 2, 3, 4, 5} is a subset of {1, 2, 3, 4, 5}.
The symbol for subset is ⊂. Thus we write:

$$\{1, 2, 3\} \subset \{1, 2, 3, 4, 5\}.$$

The number of subsets of a set depends on the number of members in the set, for example:

{a}	has 1 member and 2 subsets
{a, b}	has 2 members and 4 subsets
{a, b, c}	has 3 members and 8 subsets.

We can draw diagrams to represent sets:

$$\{1, 2, 3\} \quad \text{and} \quad \{1, 2, 3, 4, 5\}.$$

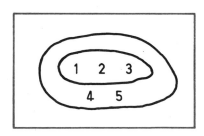

A set with no members is called the empty set and we usually write it as { }.
When two sets overlap or have common members we say the sets intersect, for example, {2, 4, 6, 8} and {1, 2, 3, 4, 5, 6} intersect and the intersection is {2, 4, 6}.
The symbol for intersection is ∩. Thus we write

$$\{2, 4, 6, 8\} \cap \{1, 2, 3, 4, 5, 6\} = \{2, 4, 6\}.$$

A diagram of the two sets {2, 4, 6, 8} and {1, 2, 3, 4, 5, 6} would be:

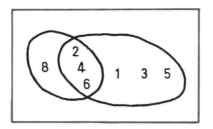

The order of a set is the number of members in that set.
The order of {1, 2, 3, 4, 5, 6} is 6.
(1) Which of the following sets have elements with some common feature? Give names to those which have.
(a) {French, German, Spanish, ---}   (b) {$\frac{1}{2}$, $\frac{2}{4}$, $\frac{3}{6}$, $\frac{4}{8}$, ---}
(c) {cotton, wool, nylon, ---}   (d) {paint, James, red, fox}.
(2) Name three members of the following sets:
(a) {teachers}   (b) {subjects you take}
(c) {hobbies you have}   (d) {natural numbers greater than 100}.
(3) Name two subsets of each of the following sets. Then draw a diagram for each.
(a) {father, mother, brother, sister}
(b) A = {w, x, y, z}   (c) {1, 2, 3, 4}.
(4) How many subsets has each of the following sets? Write out a list of the subsets for each one.
(a) {1, 2}   (b) {p, q, r}
(c) {p}   (d) {Jack, Jill}.
(5) Draw diagrams to represent the following:
(a) {1, 2, 3} ⊂ {1, 2, 3, 4, 5, 6}
(b) {p, z} ⊂ {r, p, s, t, v, z}.
(6) What is the order of each of the sets given in (3), (4), and (5)?
(7) The diagram represents two sets, C and D.

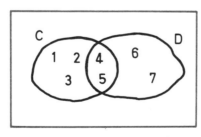

(a) List the members of set C
(b) List the members of set D
(c) Describe the set {4, 5}
(d) Describe the set {1, 2, 3}
(e) What is the order of set C and set D?

209

(8) If   E = {natural numbers less than 10}
and   F = {natural numbers greater than 7}
(a) List nine members of each set
(b) List the members of E ∩ F
(c) Draw a diagram of E and F. Label and shade in E ∩ F.

13.2
In chapter 2 you learnt about number patterns.
(1) From the set of natural numbers {1, 2, 3, 4, 5, 6, 7, 8, 9, 10, 11, 12, 13, 14, 15, 16, 17, 18, 19, 20, 21} write down the following sets of multiples. Each set must be a subset of the original set.
(a) {multiples of 3}   (b) {multiples of 2}
(c) {multiples of 7}   (d) {multiples of 21}.
(2) Write down the set of even prime numbers.
(3) Using N to stand for any natural number, write down the generalization of the following sets:
(a) {multiples of 5}   (b) {multiples of 9}
(c) {multiples of 11}   (d) {even numbers}
(e) {odd numbers}   (f) {square numbers}
(4) A generalization for the set of triangular numbers is $\frac{1}{2}n(n + 1)$.
When n = 1 we have $\frac{1}{2} \times 1 \times (1 + 1) = 1$.
This is the first triangular number.
When n = 2 we have $\frac{1}{2} \times 2 \times (2 + 1) = 3$.
This is the second triangular number.
When n = 3 we have $\frac{1}{2} \times 3 \times (3 + 1) = 6$.
This is the third triangular number.
When n = 4 we have $\frac{1}{2} \times 4 \times (4 + 1) = 10$.
This is the fourth triangular number.
Use the above generalization to write down the following triangular numbers:
(a) the ninth   (b) the tenth
(c) the twentieth   (d) the hundredth.
(5) The sum of the first two odd numbers is the second square number: 1 + 3 = 4.
The sum of the first three odd numbers is the third square number:
1 + 3 + 5 = 9.
The sum of the first four odd numbers is the fourth square number:
1 + 3 + 5 + 7 = 16.
Find the following sums of odd numbers:
(a) the first six   (b) the first nine
(c) the first seventeen   (d) the first forty.
(6) Use the appropriate generalization to find the following even numbers:
(a) the seventh   (b) the one hundred and first.

(7) Write down the answers to the following squares:

$$1^2 = \qquad\qquad 11^2 =$$
$$111^2 = \qquad\qquad 1{,}111^2 =$$

(a) Find a pattern from the above answers and use it to write down $11{,}111{,}111^2$, and $111{,}111{,}111^2$.
(b) Investigate what happens to the pattern when the number of ones in the number is greater than nine.
(8) Repeat (7) for the following squares:

$$9^2 = \qquad\qquad 99^2 =$$
$$999^2 = \qquad\qquad 9{,}999^2 =$$

Find a pattern and use it to write down the following squares: $9{,}999{,}999^2$ and $999{,}999{,}999^2$.
(9) Find the next three members of each of these sets:
(a) $\{4, 13, 22, 31, 40, \text{---}\}$
the set of multiples of 4 in base five
(b) $\{6, 15, 24, 33, 42, 51, 60, \text{---}\}$
the set of multiples of 6 in base seven
(c) $\{5, 14, 23, 32, 41, 50, \text{---}\}$
the set of multiples of 5 in base six
(d) $\{9, 18, 27, 36, 45, 54, 63, 72, 81, 90, \text{---}\}$
the set of multiples of 9 in base ten.
(10) Write down the answers to the following:

$$1^2 - 0^2 = \qquad\qquad 2^2 - 1^2 =$$
$$3^2 - 2^2 = \qquad\qquad 4^2 - 3^2 =$$

To what set of numbers do the answers belong?
(11) Write down the answers to the following:

$$3^2 + 4^2 = \qquad\qquad 6^2 + 8^2 =$$
$$9^2 + 12^2 = \qquad\qquad 12^2 + 16^2 =$$

(a) The answers are all square numbers, write them in the form N^2. For example 36 would be written 6^2, 49 would be written 7^2, etc.
(b) Can you see any pattern in your answers?

13.3

In chapter 3 you learnt about shape.
(1) What is a line of symmetry?
(2) Do all things have lines of symmetry?

(3) Sketch the following and mark in any lines of symmetry:

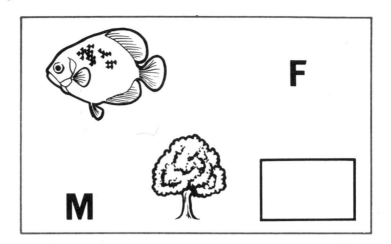

(4) Give three members of the following sets, each member must have at least one line of symmetry.
(a) {capital letters of the alphabet}   (b) {cutlery}
(c) {natural numbers less than 10}   (d) {things to eat}.
(5) How many lines of symmetry has a square?
(6) How many lines of symmetry has a rectangle?
(7) Below are shown three triangles. How many lines of symmetry has each?

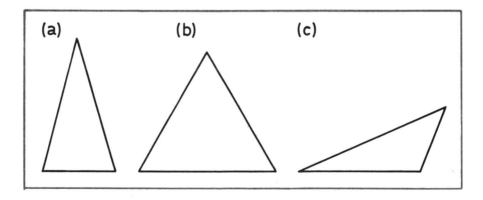

(8) In how many ways can each of the shapes of (5), (6), and (7) be cut from a folded sheet of paper?
(9) If the dotted line in the following diagram is a line of symmetry, what can you say about:
(a) the two blue lines   (b) the two fine black lines?
Are there any other pairs of lines similar to the blue and the fine black lines?

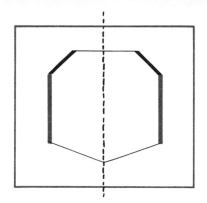

(10) How many rectangles can you count in the following grid?
(There are a lot more than twelve.)

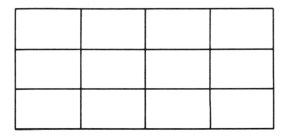

(11) How many of the triangles in the following diagram contain the dot?

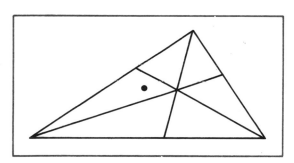

(12) What are tessellations?

(13) We used various shapes to cover surfaces. Here are a few of the shapes that we used:

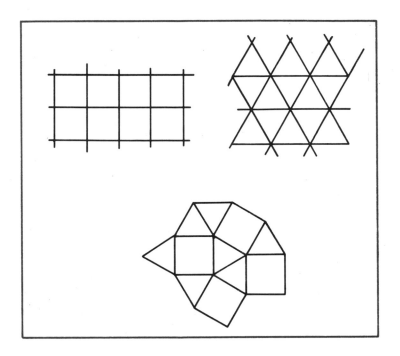

There are also several letters of the alphabet which are suitable for this. Two examples are shown below:

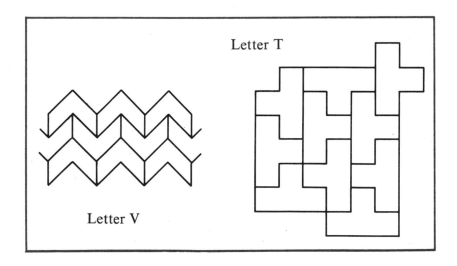

See if you can find any more letters which will tessellate.

Chapter 4 dealt with the use of 'larger than', 'smaller than', and
'between'. Almost everything we use or have is either smaller than
or larger than something else.
The symbol for 'smaller than' is $<$.
The symbol for 'larger than' is $>$.
(1) Insert the symbol $<$ or $>$ in the following to make a true statement.
(a) 11   9   (b) 7   4   (c) 3   7
(d) 6   11   (e) 2   1   (f) 17   5.
(2) Which of the following statements are true?
(a) $7 > 11$ (b) $14 < 17$ (c) $6 > 5$
(d) $18 > 19$ (e) $54 < 55$ (f) $16 < 15$.
(3) If $x < 5$ what possible values can x have $(x \in N^+)$? What is the
solution set of x?
(4) If $x > 7$ what possible values can x have $(x \in N^+)$? What is the
solution set of x?
(5) Draw this number line:
Mark on it the solution sets to (3) and (4).

(6) Find the solution set for each of the following $(x \in N^+)$:
(a) $x < 7$ (b) $x > 6$ (c) $x > 57$
(d) $x < 1$ (e) $x > 0$ (f) $x < 3$.
(7) Draw one number line and mark on it the solution sets for (6)
(a) and (b).
(8) What is the intersection of the two sets in (6) (a) and (b)?
(9) If $x + 1 < 4$ what possible values can x have $(x \in N^+)$? What is
the solution set of x? Draw a number line and mark on it the
solution set.
(10) Give the solution set to each of the following $(x \in N^+)$:
(a) $x + 1 < 7$ (b) $x + 1 > 4$ (c) $x + 2 < 7$
(d) $x + 2 > 4$ (e) $x + 7 < 9$ (f) $x + 5 > 14$
(g) $x + 4 < 5$ (h) $x + 4 > 4$.
(11) If $2x > 3$ what values can x have $(x \in N^+)$? What is the solution set of x? Draw a number line and mark on it the solution set.
(12) Give the solution set to each of the following $(x \in N^+)$:
(a) $2x < 5$ (b) $2x < 10$ (c) $2x > 7$
(d) $3x > 6$ (e) $5x < 15$ (f) $5x > 10$.
(13) If $2x + 1 < 6$ what values can x have $(x \in N^+)$? What is the

solution set of x? Draw a number line and mark on it the solution set.

(14) Give the solution set to each of the following ($x \in N^+$):

(a) $2x + 2 < 6$ (b) $2x + 3 > 4$ (c) $2x + 3 < 6$

(d) $3x + 2 < 9$ (e) $3x + 3 > 10$ (f) $3x + 1 > 1$.

We know that 2 is between 1 and 3; we also know that $1 < 2$ and $2 < 3$, so we write $1 < 2 < 3$.

(15) By putting in $<$ or $>$ make the following into true statements:

(a) 6   7   8   (b) 5   4   3   (c) 7   11   13

(d) 15   12   9   (e) 4   2   0   (f) 5   6   12.

(16) If $4 < x < 7$ what values can x have ($x \in N^+$)? What is the solution set of x? Draw a number line and mark on it the solution set.

(17) Give the solution set for each of the following ($x \in N^+$):

(a) $3 < x < 7$ (b) $8 < x < 15$

(c) $14 > x > 2$ (d) $2 < 2x < 8$

(e) $12 > 3x > 1$ (f) $4 < x + 2 < 8$

(g) $8 < 2x + 1 < 15$ (h) $12 > 3x + 2 > 2$.

13.5

In chapter 5 you learnt that a composition table is a convenient way of showing how a set of elements behaves under a given operation.

Make out composition tables for the following sets of numbers under the operations given. In each case say to what set of numbers, the numbers inside the table belong.

(1) $\{2, 4, 6, 8\}$ $\{1, 3, 5, 7\}$ under the operation of addition

(2) $\{1, 3, 5, 7\}$ $\{3, 5, 7, 9\}$ under the operation of addition

(3) $\{2, 4, 6, 8\}$ $\{2, 8, 12, 20\}$ under the operation of addition

(4) $\{2, 4, 6, 8\}$ $\{2, 8, 12, 20\}$ under the operation of multiplication

(5) $\{1, 3, 5, 7\}$ $\{3, 5, 7, 9\}$ under the operation of multiplication

(6) $\{1, 3, 5, 7\}$ $\{2, 4, 6, 8\}$ under the operation of multiplication.

(7) Make out a composition table for $\{E, O\}$ under the operation of (a) addition and (b) multiplication. Let E stand for 'even number' and O for 'odd number'.

(8) Two dice are thrown and the sum of their scores noted. In your notebook, complete the composition table shown below, filling in the sums of the scores of the dice. One of the values has been filled in for you.

Second die							
6							
5							
4							
3							9
2							
1							
+	1	2	3	4	5	6	First die

Composition table showing all possible sums of two dice

Use your composition table to answer the following questions:
(9) How many possible ways are there of combining the scores of the two dice? Take a six with the first die and a three with the second die, to be different from a six with the second die and a three with the first die, etc.
(10) How many possible ways are there of scoring a four with the two dice?
(11) How many possible ways are there of scoring a twelve with the two dice?
(12) What other score is as elusive as twelve?
(13) What is the most likely score?
(14) How many possible ways are there of scoring under seven?
(15) How many possible ways are there of scoring nine or more?
(16) Which score is most likely to occur – seven or nine?
(17) How many possible ways are there of scoring more than five but less than eight?
(18) How many possible ways are there of scoring two?
(19) How many possible ways are there of scoring three or less?
(20) How many possible ways are there of scoring four or less?
(21) How many possible ways are there of scoring five or less?
(22) How many possible ways are there of scoring six or less?
(23) How many possible ways are there of scoring seven or less?
(24) Look at your answers to (18) to (23). All your answers belong to at least two sets; one is the set of natural numbers, can you name the other?

13.6
In chapter 6 you found some strange arithmetic.
(1) In the normal method of counting we use base ——— ?

13.6

(2) When we use base five for counting, five is represented by ——— ?

(3) What is a composition table?

(4) The digits used in counting in base eight are ——— ?

(5) Try the following:

(a) 23
    +14
    ——— base 6

(b) 16
    +21
    ——— base 7

(c) 52
    −47
    ——— base 8

(d) 23
    −16
    ——— base 9

(e) 13
    × 2
    ——— base 4

(f) 12
    × 3
    ——— base 4

(g) 3)12
    ——— base 4

(h) 2131
    +1231
    ———— base 4

(i) Find the next number in the series 3, 10, 13, 20.

(j) Find x if x + 3 = 14 (base 6).

(6) Complete this composition table (base 5):

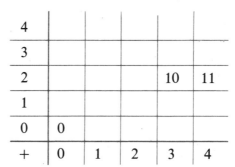

4					
3					
2				10	11
1					
0	0				
+	0	1	2	3	4

(7) Find the units in the following:

(a) 2   1
    +3   4
    ———————
     5   5

(b) 3   25
    −1   40
    ———————
     1   45

(8) (a) Change 2·75 kilogrammes to grammes.

(b) Change 5200 millimetres to metres.

Simplify: (c) *Kg*
              2·96
            +3·14
            ————

(d) *Km*
    3·97
   −2·69
   ————

(e) £
   9·75
  −8·96
  ————

(f) What is 4700 metres in kilometres?

218

(9) Find x in each of these statements
(a)   31 (base 6) = 25 (base x)
(b)   31 (base x) = 14 (base 12)
(c) 213 (base 4) = 33 (base x)
(d)   x (base 8) = 13 (base 4)
(e) 101 (base 2) =   x (base 6)

(10) (a) Mary has 36*p* pocket money per week. Each week she saves half of it and buys her dog a 3*p* bar of chocolate. How much does she have to spend on herself?
(b) Mrs Jones has £9 per week housekeeping. She spends two thirds of it on food and two thirds of what is left on rent. How much rent does she pay?
(c) A boy has 25*p* pocket money per week. If he cleans his father's car on Saturday he can double his pocket money. If he runs an errand for the neighbour he can increase his pocket money by one-fifth of the original amount. In a certain week he ran an errand and cleaned his father's car. How much money did he receive altogether?

13.7
In chapter 7 you learnt about balancing.
(1) What is the golden rule of the balance?
(2) Are the following balanced?

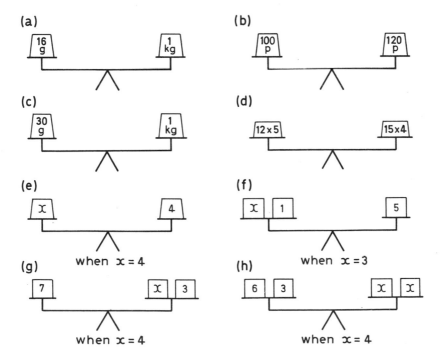

219

(3) Write down the equations of the following balances:

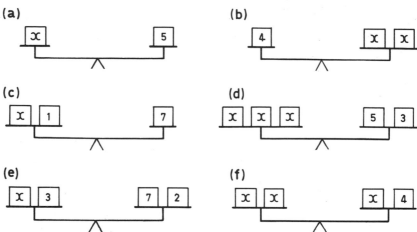

(a)   (b)

(c)   (d)

(e)   (f)

The golden rule of equations (and therefore of balances) is, 'If we do something to one side we must do the same thing to the other side if we wish to preserve equality.'

(4) Use the golden rule to help you solve the following equations. Write down each step of your solution on a new line.

(a) $x + 3 = 7$ (b) $x + 11 = 15$

(c) $x + 6 = 4 + 3$ (d) $x + 5 = 5$

(e) $7 + 11 = x + 9$ (f) $x + 17 = 21$

(g) $x + 3 + 14 = 27 - 6$ (h) $34 = x + 17$.

(5) Solve the following equations:

(a) $x + x = 6$ (b) $2x = 8$

(c) $x + x + x = 9$ (d) $3x = 12$

(e) $8 = 2x$ (f) $4 + 6 = 2x$

(g) $3x = 17 + 4$ (h) $12x = 72$.

(6) Solve the following equations:

(a) $2x + 2 = 6$ (b) $2x + 5 = 7$

(c) $3x + 6 = 15$ (d) $4x + 5 = 9$

(e) $3x + x = 16$ (f) $12 + 2 = 4x + 3x$

(g) $3x = 5 + 4$ (h) $9x = 16 + x$

(i) $2x + 12 = 8x$ (j) $7x + 5 = x + 11$

(k) $4x + 5 = 3x + 8$ (l) $2x + 12 = 5x + 3$

(m) $3x + x = 18 + 2x$ (n) $7x + 2 = 3x + x + 8$.

(7) First write down an equation for each of the following problems and then solve the equations. (Let the value you have to find be x.)

(a) Janet and John were selling tickets for the school play. John sold eight tickets more than Janet. Together they sold twenty-four tickets. How many did they each sell?

(b) Peter is twice as old as Jane. Together their ages add up to twenty-one. How old is Jane?

In chapter 8 you learnt that when using ordered pairs in graphical work, it is usual to put the number which refers to the horizontal axis, first, and the number which refers to the vertical axis, second. Thus in (x, y), x refers to the horizontal distance travelled to get to the point and y refers to the vertical distance travelled. Ordered pairs of this type are called *cartesian co-ordinates* after René Descartes, the French mathematician and philosopher who invented them.

If a point lies on a line then, the ordered pair representing the point balances the equation of the line.

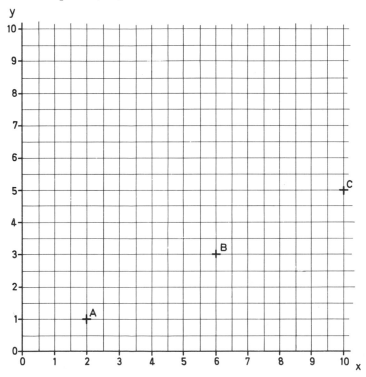

(1) Write down the ordered pairs which represent the points A, B, and C in the diagram above.

(2) Write down the equation of the line passing through all three points.

(3) Does the point (0, 0) lie on this line?

(4) Does the point (5, $2\frac{1}{2}$) lie on this line?

(5) Does the point (1, 10) lie on the line represented by the equation $x + y = 9$?

(6) Does the point (2, 6) lie on the line represented by the equation $x + y = 11$?

(7) Do the points represented by the ordered pairs in the left-hand

column below, lie on the lines represented by the equations in the right-hand column?

Point	Line
(a) (3, 4)	$x + y = 7$
(b) (12, 6)	$x - y = 6$
(c) (4, 5)	$x - y = 1$
(d) (4, 5)	$y - x = 1$
(e) (4, 5)	$2x + y = 13$
(f) (10, 20)	$y = 2x$
(g) (10, 20)	$y - 10 = x$

(8) Do the lines represented by the equations in the left-hand column below, pass through the points represented by the ordered pairs in the right-hand column? Answer yes or no.

(a) $y = 5x$	(2, 10)
(b) $y = 2x - 3$	(5, 6)
(c) $2x + 3y = 16$	(2, 4)
(d) $4x - 2y = 0$	(10, 5)
(e) $y = \frac{1}{2}x + 2$	$(7, 5\frac{1}{2})$
(f) $y = \frac{1}{2}x + 2$	(12, 8)

State which of the following are true:
(9) the point represented by (3, 4) belongs to $\{(x, y)/x + y > 2\}$
(10) the point represented by (4, 6) belongs to $\{(x, y)/x + y < 9\}$
(11) the point represented by (3, 7) belongs to $\{(x, y)/2x + y < 13\}$
(12) the point represented by (7, 3) belongs to $\{(x, y)/x + 2y > 13\}$
(13) the point represented by (7, 4) belongs to $\{(x, y)/x + 2y > 13\}$.

13.9
In chapter 9 you learnt many things about area.
(1) A rectangle is built of twelve one-centimetre squares. List the members of the set $\{(l, b)/l \times b = 12\}$ where l and b are the length and breadth of the rectangles which can be made from the twelve one-centimetre squares.
(2) The area of a rectangle is sixty-four square centimetres. Using whole numbers only for l and b, list the possible values of the perimeter of the rectangle. What shape will the rectangle have when the perimeter has its smallest value?
(3) and (4) Find the number of one-centimetre squares needed to cover each of the following shapes:

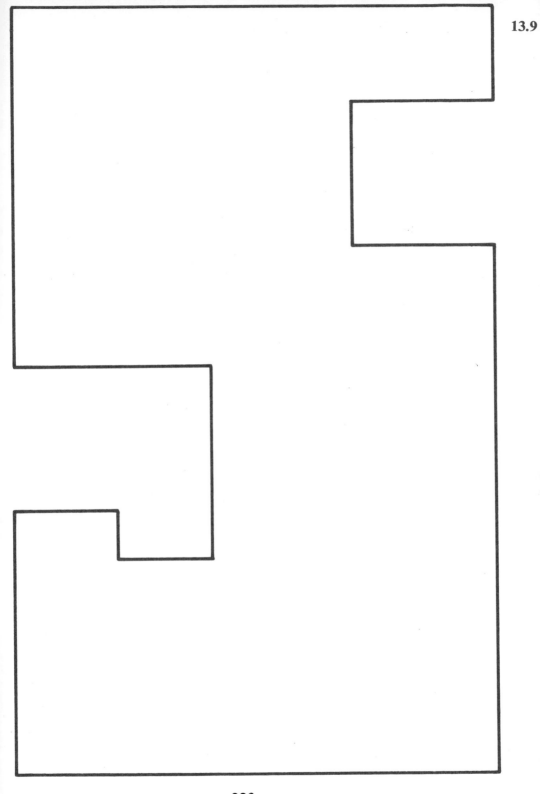

13.9

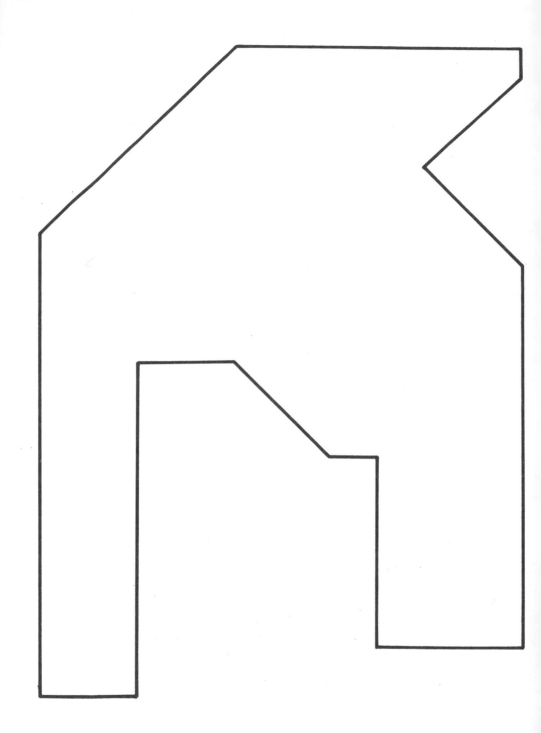

(5) How many five-millimetre squares would be needed to cover each of them?

(6) A room is this shape:

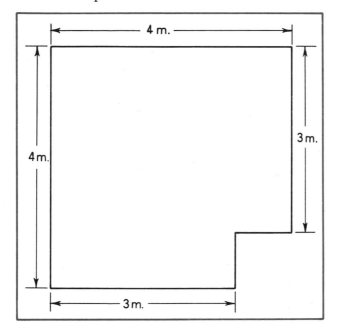

(a) What is its area in square metres?

(b) What will it cost to cover the floor of the room with carpet, if carpet costs £3 per square metre?

Find the area of each of these figures, lengths are in metres:

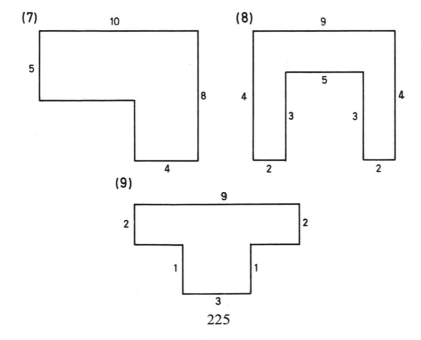

(7)

(8)

(9)

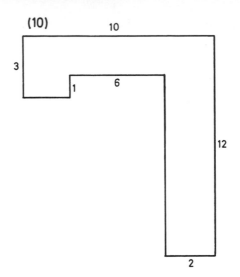

13.10

In chapter 10 you learnt the following terms; do you remember what they mean? Proper fractions, improper fractions, equivalent fractions, mixed numbers, numerator, and denominator.

Write down three fractions equivalent to each of the following:

(1) $\frac{1}{2}$ (2) $\frac{1}{3}$ (3) $\frac{4}{5}$ (4) $\frac{18}{20}$.

(5) If A = {fractions equivalent to $\frac{3}{5}$} and
     B = {fractions equivalent to $\frac{1}{4}$}, find A ∩ B.

Find the answers to the following:

(6) $\frac{2}{3} + \frac{1}{2}$ (7) $\frac{4}{7} + \frac{1}{2}$ (8) $1 + \frac{4}{5}$

(9) $3 - \frac{3}{4}$ (10) $2\frac{1}{6} - 1\frac{2}{3}$ (11) $3\frac{2}{3} - 1$.

Change the following improper fractions to mixed numbers:

(12) $\frac{5}{4}$ (13) $\frac{19}{7}$ (14) $\frac{4}{3}$ (15) $\frac{15}{6}$.

Change the following mixed numbers to improper fractions:

(16) $3\frac{2}{7}$ (17) $5\frac{1}{4}$ (18) $4\frac{1}{9}$ (19) $2\frac{3}{5}$.

(20) Which is the smallest of these fractions: $\frac{5}{12}, \frac{1}{3}, \frac{1}{4}, \frac{3}{8}$?

What value must x have if:

(21) $x + \frac{1}{2} = 2$?   (22) $x + \frac{1}{3} = \frac{2}{3}$?

(23) $x + \frac{1}{4} = \frac{3}{4}$?   (24) $\frac{1}{2} - x = \frac{1}{4}$?

(25) A boy has 12p pocket money, he spends half of this on sweets. How much is left?

(26) A girl has 20p pocket money, she spends one-quarter of this on ribbon and one-third of what is left on sweets. The remainder she saves. How much does she save?

What is the next term in each of these series and the general term?

(27) $\frac{1}{1}, \frac{1}{2}, \frac{1}{3}, \frac{1}{4},$ ---   (28) $\frac{1}{2}, \frac{1}{4}, \frac{1}{6}, \frac{1}{8},$ ---

(29) $\frac{1}{1}, \frac{1}{3}, \frac{1}{5},$ ---   (30) $\frac{1}{2}, \frac{2}{3}, \frac{3}{4}, \frac{4}{5},$ ---.

In chapter 11 you learnt some very important facts about angles.
An acute angle is greater than 0° and less than 90°.
A right angle is equal to 90°.
An obtuse angle is greater than 90° but less than 180°.
Two right angles fit together to make a straight line.
A reflex angle is greater than 180° and less than 360°.
If the sum of a number of angles is 180°, the angles are said to be
supplementary. If two angles are supplementary, then each angle is
said to be the supplement of the other. For example, 30° is the
supplement of 150°, and 150° is the supplement of 30°.
If the sum of a number of angles is 90°, then the angles are said to
be complementary. If the sum of two angles is 90° then one angle is
said to be the complement of the other. Thus, 70° is the complement
of 20°, and 20° is the complement of 70°.
The angles of a triangle are supplementary.
(1) State the type of angle, for each of the angles listed below, giving
your answer from {acute angle, right angle, obtuse angle, reflex
angle}.

(a) 30°   (b) 120°   (c) 137°
(d) 215°   (e) 156°   (f) 167°
(g) 92°   (h) 45°   (i) 275°.

(2) (a)
What is angle θ?

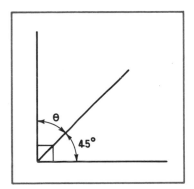

(b)
ABD is a straight line; find angle θ.

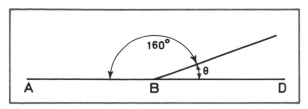

13.11   (c)

BCD is a straight line; find angle θ.

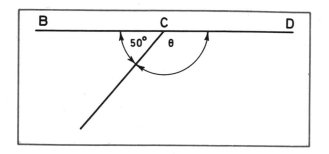

(3) Estimate the size of the three angles on the right:

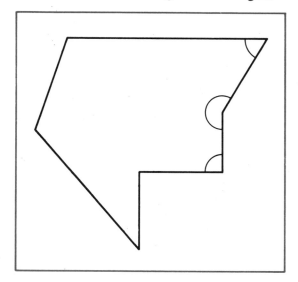

(4) Write down the supplements of the following angles:
(a) 130°   (b) 127°   (c) 36°   (d) 41°
(e) 123°   (f) 28°   (g) 161°   (h) 113°.
(5) Write down the complements of the following angles:
(a) 31°   (b) 12°   (c) 89°   (d) 3°
(e) 45°   (f) 51°   (g) 63°   (h) 27°.
(6) Use your protractor to measure the following angles:

(a)   **(b)**   **(c)**

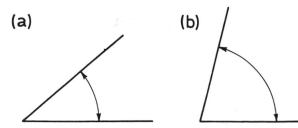

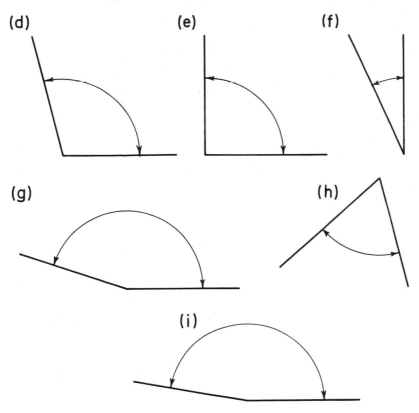

(7) Write down the number of degrees in the interior angles of the following figures:
(a) an equilateral triangle (three angles)
(b) an isosceles right-angled triangle (three angles)
(c) a square (four angles)
(d) a rectangle (four angles)
(e) a regular pentagon (five angles)
(f) a regular hexagon (six angles)
(g) a regular octagon (eight angles).
(8) Find angles α and θ in the following diagrams:

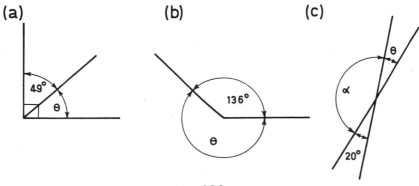

13.11

(d)

(e)

(f)

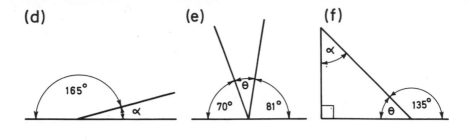

(g)

(h)

(i)

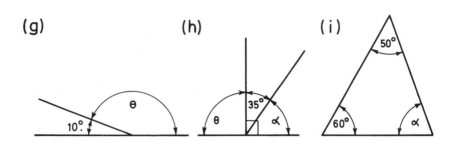

(j)

(k)

(l)

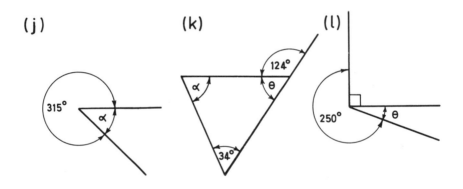

(9) Look at the diagrams above and answer the following:

(a) what can you say about the angles θ and 49° in (a)?

(b) what can you say about the angles 70°, θ, and 81° in (e)?

(c) what can you say about the angles θ and 124° in (k)?

(d) what can you say about the angles θ, α, and 35° in (h)?

(e) what can you say about the angles (34° + α) and 124° in (k)?

(f) what can you say about the angles α and θ in (f)?

(g) what can you say about the angles 20° and θ in (c)?

(h) what can you say about the angles α and θ in (h)?

(i) what can you say about the angles θ and 136° in (b)?

(j) what can you say about the angles (90° + α) and 135° in (f)?

(10) Can you see any connections between the answers to (9)(e) and (9)(j), and the respective diagrams?

230

(11) Give the angles between the following points of the compass:

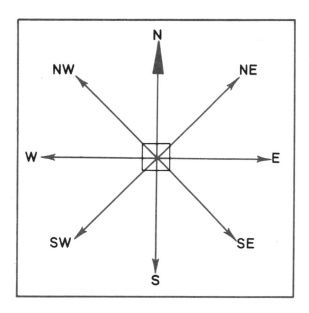

(a) the two angles between N and E
(b) the two angles between W and S
(c) the acute angle between N and NE
(d) the acute angle between SW and S
(e) the obtuse angle between NW and E
(f) the obtuse angle between SE and N
(g) the reflex angle between SE and N
(h) the obtuse angle between W and NE
(i) the reflex angle between W and NE
(j) the reflex angle between E and SE.

13.12
In chapter 12 you learnt that a pictogram is a convenient way of presenting statistics.
(1) Draw a pictogram to represent this information:

Shop	Number of T.V. sets sold in one day
Smith's	3
Jones'	1
Baker's	4

(2) The number of children at a school increases in the following way:

Year	1964	1965	1966	1967
Number of children	800	900	1,000	1,100

Represent this information in a pictogram using one pin-man to stand for 100 children.

(3) Look at this pictogram and then answer the questions below:

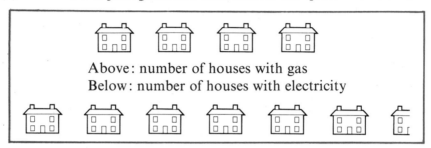

If one drawing of a house is equivalent to 100 houses, how many houses have gas? How many houses have electricity?

(4) A census is taken in a certain area and a pictogram plotted of the results:

Number of families with:	One man represents six families
no children	🚶 🚶 🚶
1 child	🚶 🚶 🚶 🚶 🚶
2 children	🚶 🚶 🚶 🚶 🚶 🚶 🚶 🚶
3 children	🚶 🚶 🚶 🚶
4 children	🚶 🚶 🚶
5 children	🚶

How many families have no children, one child, two children, three children, four children, and five children?

232

Test Papers

Test paper 1

(1) How many degrees are there in: (a) a quarter turn (b) one-twelfth of a turn?

(2) What is the next number in each of these series:

(a) 1, 4, 7, 10, --- (base 10)   (b) 1, 5, 10, 14, ---? (base 9)

(3) Find the value of x in each of these equations:

(a) $x + 7 = 16$ (b) $2x + 9 = 17$.

(4) Are the following correct?

(a)
```
   43
 - 26
 ─────
   14  (base 7)
```

(b)
```
   26
 ×  2
 ─────
   55  (base 7)
```

(5) (a) What do you understand by a line of symmetry?

(b) AB is to be a line of symmetry:

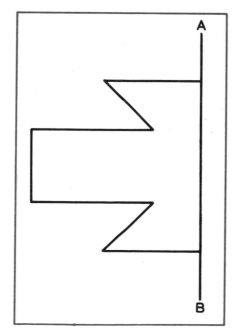

Copy the figure on to squared paper and draw the other half. Has the figure another line of symmetry? If so, mark it in.

233

(6) (a) If   A = {1, 3, 5, 7, 9, ---}
    and   B = {3, 6, 9, 12, 15, ---}
what is A ∩ B?
(b) Describe set A in words.   (c) Describe set B in words.

Test paper 2
(1) Find the angles marked x and y in these figures:

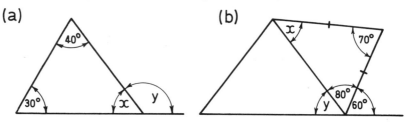

(a)   (b)

(2) Find x from these equations:
(a) $x + 6 = 14$ (b) $3x + 7 = x + 15$.
(3) Copy and complete this composition table:

3			11	
2			10	
1	1			
0				
+	0	1	2	3

What base is it worked in?
(4) Fit units to these:
(a) 3)2   1   0   (b)   3   40   20
　　　 16   20   ×4
　　　　　　　　　　　　　　　　　　　────────────
　　　　　　　　　　　　　　　　　　　14   41   20

(5) (a) How many lines of symmetry has a regular four-sided figure (a square)?
(b) How many lines of symmetry has a regular octagon?
(c) How many lines of symmetry has a regular n-gon?
(6) Construct this triangle using a ruler, protractor, and compasses.

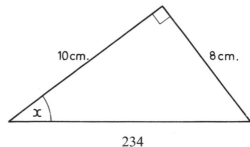

10cm.   8cm.

x

(a) Measure the angle x.
(b) What is the area of the triangle?

Test paper 3
(1) What natural numbers satisfy these inequalities?
(a) $3 < x < 9$ call them set A
(b) $4 < x + 1 < 10$ call them set B
(c) $5 < 2x + 1 < 12$ call them set C.
What is:
(d) $A \cap B$?   (e) $A \cap B \cap C$?
(2) Pick out from this table:
(a) the multiples of 3 less than 30
(b) the multiples of 7 greater than 63

1	2	3	4	5	6	7	8	9	10
11	12	13	14	15	16	17	18	19	20
21	22	23	24	25	26	27	28	29	30
31	32	33	34	35	36	37	38	39	40
41	42	43	44	45	46	47	48	49	50
51	52	53	54	55	56	57	58	59	60
61	62	63	64	65	66	67	68	69	70
71	72	73	74	75	76	77	78	79	80
81	82	83	84	85	86	87	88	89	90
91	92	93	94	95	96	97	98	99	100

(c) the square numbers
(d) seven prime numbers less than 30
(e) three triangular numbers less than 30.

(3) Find the area of each of these shapes:

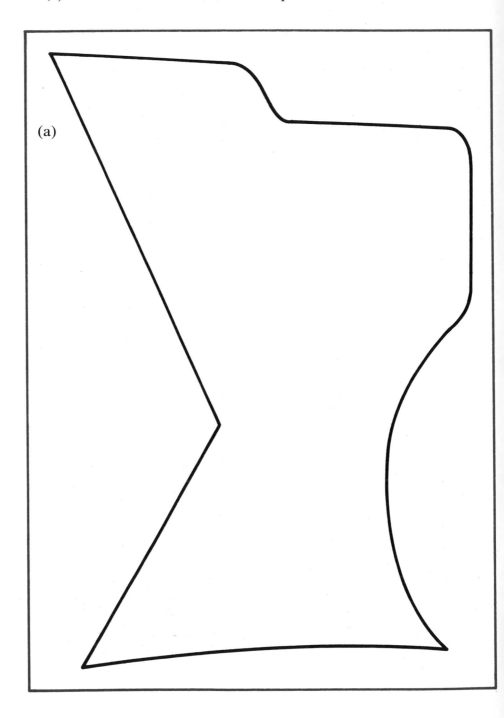

(a)

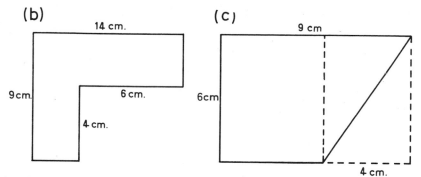

(b) **14 cm.** 9cm. 6 cm. 4 cm.

(c) 9 cm 6cm 4 cm.

(d) What is the perimeter of the shape in (b)?

(4) (a) What are the ordered pairs representing the points marked in this diagram?

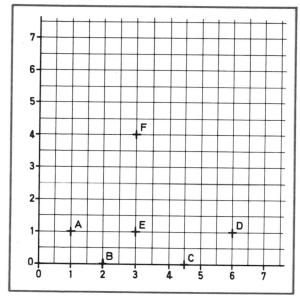

(b) Plot these points on graph paper.

(c) Join them up as follows:

A to B to C to D to A   A to E to F to A   E to D to F to E.

(d) Estimate as accurately as you can the area of FABCD in square units.

(5) Measure these angles:

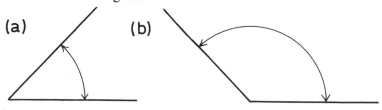

(a)   (b)

How would you describe each of them?

(6) (a) Find (i) $1\frac{1}{2} + 3\frac{1}{4}$ (ii) $2\frac{1}{3} - 1\frac{1}{6}$.
(b) Change $2\frac{1}{6}$ to an improper fraction.
(c) Change $\frac{15}{9}$ to a mixed number in its simplest form.

Test paper 4
(1) (a) Plot on graph paper the set of ordered pairs (x, y) which fit
this equation: $xy = 12$.
(b) Your graph should look like this:

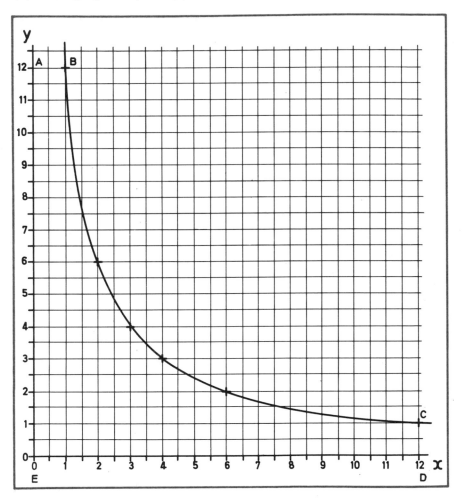

Estimate the area ABCDE in square units.

(2) If $2\triangle = \square$, does this balance?

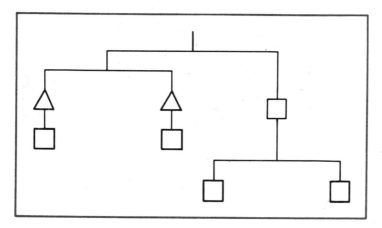

(3) (a) Copy and complete this table:

3			4	10	
2				4	
1				3	
0					
+	0	1	2	3	

(b) In what base is it worked?
(c) Does the table have a line of symmetry? If so which numbers lie on it?
(4) If a rectangular sheet of paper is folded in half, in half again, and in half again, and then opened out, how many small rectangles will there be on the paper?

239

(5) This pictogram represents a milk roundsman's sales one Saturday:

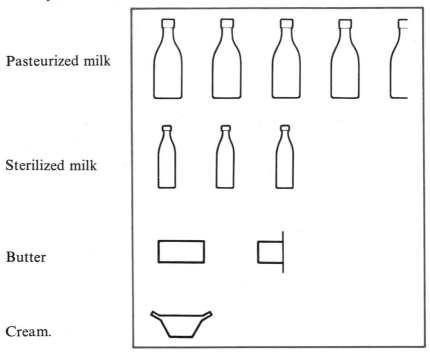

Pasteurized milk

Sterilized milk

Butter

Cream.

(a) If each diagram represents 100 bottles, tubs, or packets, how many bottles, tubs, and packets did he sell?
(b) If the pasteurized milk is sold at 5p per bottle, how much money does he collect for pasteurized milk?
(6) (a) A man earning £12 per week is offered a rise of £3. What fraction is the rise of his original wage?
(b) He gave two-thirds of his original wage to his wife for house-keeping, he decided to increase this by one-quarter. How much housekeeping money does he give his wife now?
(c) He gave his son 50p pocket money from his original wage. He decides to increase this by one-quarter. How much does his son now receive?
(d) How much extra money does the man have in his pocket after paying his wife and son these increases?

Test paper 5
(1) Change the number 234 (base 5) to the following bases:
(a) base 10   (b) base 3.
(2) Fill in the space in the ordered pairs so that they satisfy the equation given:

(a) $\{(1, \quad), (2, \quad), (\quad, 8), (3, \quad), (\quad, 0)\}$
satisfy the equation $x + y = 10$

(b) $\{(12, \quad), (10, \quad), (\quad, 1), (\quad, 2), (\quad, 3)\}$
satisfy the equation $x - y = 4$.

(3) Write down the equation between x and y satisfied by the following sets of ordered pairs:

(a) $\{(2, 4), (3, 6), (4, 8), (5, 10), ---\}$

(b) $\{(1, 3), (2, 4), (3, 5), (7, 9), (16, 18), ---\}$.

(4) $A = \{a, b, c, d, e, f\}$
$B = \{a, c, d, h, i, j\}$
$C = \{a, e, f\}$.

Write down the following sets:

(a) $A \cap B$ (b) $B \cap C$ (c) $A \cap C$ (d) $A \cap B \cap C$.

(5) Simplify: (a) $2 \cdot 9 \, m + 3 \, km$ (b) hr   min   sec

                                4   30   17

                                         $\times 6$

(c) £9·60 ÷ 5   (d) $\frac{1}{4}$ of 2 m 40 cm.

(6) (a) The angles of a triangle are 9x, 6x, and 3x. What is the value of x?

(b) Simplify (i) $1\frac{3}{7} + 2\frac{2}{9}$; (ii) $4\frac{3}{5} - 2\frac{1}{3}$

Test paper 6

(1) Estimate the size of the following angles:

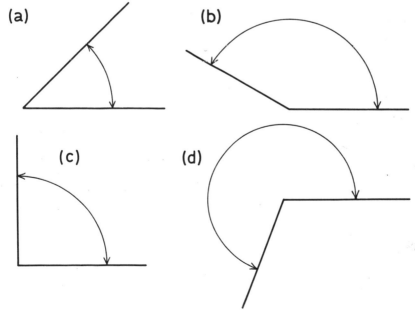

(a)   (b)

(c)   (d)

In each case state whether the angles are acute, obtuse, reflex, etc.

(2) (a) What is a tessellation?
(b) Sketch two examples using any shapes you wish.
(3) (a) What does the symbol $\subset$ stand for?
(b) If A = {square, rectangle, triangle} what is the order of set A?
(c) Is {square, triangle} a subset of set A?
(4) Plot the line x + y = 12 and write down the ordered pair of the point where the line crosses the x axis.
(5) Find the value of
(a) $\frac{1}{2} + \frac{3}{4}$ (b) $2\frac{1}{4} - 1\frac{1}{8}$ (c) $4\frac{1}{5} + 2\frac{3}{10}$.
(6) (a) The area of a rectangle is 24 cm^2. List the possible values of the length and breadth as ordered pairs.
(b) Change the ordered pairs of (a) to base 6.

Test paper 7
(1) (a) What symbol stands for 'less than'?
By using < or > complete the following:
(b) 7   6 (c) 4   8 (d) 3   11.
(2) (a) If A = {Jack, Queen, King}
    and B = {Ace, Queen}
draw a diagram to represent A and B.
(b) Shade in A $\cap$ B.
(3) Solve the following equations:
(a) 3x = 3 (b) x + 4 = 4
(c) 2x = 6 (d) 3x + 2 = 8.
(4) (a) Which digits are used in base four arithmetic?
(b) How do we represent four in base four arithmetic?
(c) Change each of the following base four numbers into base ten numbers: 11, 22, 100, 121.
(5) (a) What are complementary angles?
(b) What are supplementary angles?
(c) In the following sets of angles state which are complementary and which supplementary:
(i) {60°, 30°} (ii) {150°, 30°} (iii) {80°, 90°} (iv) {10°, 70°, 100°}
(6) Find the solution sets for:
(a) A = {0 < x < 10, x $\in$ N}
(b) B = {0 < 2x < 10, x $\in$ N}.
(c) Mark the sets on a number line
(d) What is A $\cap$ B? (e) Is B $\subset$ A?

Test paper 8
(1) How many degrees are there in:
(a) one-quarter of a complete turn
(b) half of a complete turn

(c) three-eighths of a complete turn?

(d) Name the three types of angle in (a), (b), and (c).

(2) (a) List the first four members of the sets:

$\quad\quad$ A = {square numbers} $\quad\quad$ B = {triangular numbers}.

(b) What is A ∩ B?

(3) (a) How many squares can you find in the following diagram:

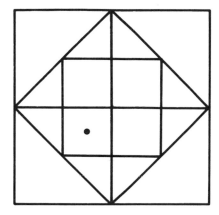

(b) How many squares contain the dot?

(4) (a) Find the value of x if 3x + 4 = 10.

(b) Find the solution set for x if $0 < 2x + 1 < 10 \, (x \in N^+)$

(c) Find the value of (i) $\frac{5}{8} + \frac{3}{4}$ (ii) $1\frac{1}{2} + 2\frac{5}{8}$.

(5) A photographer's shop sells the following cameras in the first six months of the year:

January	five,	February	five,
March	ten,	April	twenty-five,
May	thirty-five,	June	fifty.

Represent this information in the form of a pictogram.

Why do you think the sales were so low during the first three months?

Would you expect sales to go on increasing for the remainder of the year?

(6)

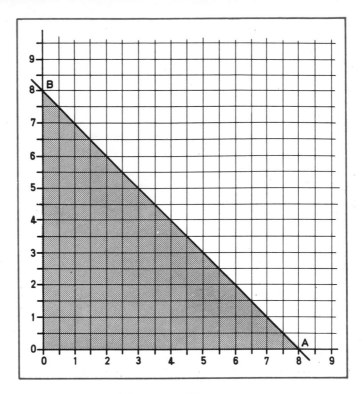

This represents a five millimetre grid.
(a) Has the triangle any lines of symmetry? If so, mark them in.
(b) How many five-millimetre squares are needed to cover the triangle exactly?
(c) What is the area of the triangle in square centimetres?
(d) What are the ordered pairs for points A and B?
(e) What is the equation for the line AB?
(f) Are the three angles of the triangle complementary or supplementary?

PRINTED AND BOUND IN GREAT BRITAIN BY
WILLIAM CLOWES AND SONS, LIMITED, LONDON AND BECCLES